Grade 2 Writing

Contents

Practice each letter.
ABCDEF
A A A
B B B
C C C
D D D
E E E
F F F
GEOGRAPHY
GEOGRAPHY
101200.00

GHIJKLM

G G G

H H H

I I I

J J J

K K K

L L L

M M M

Honey

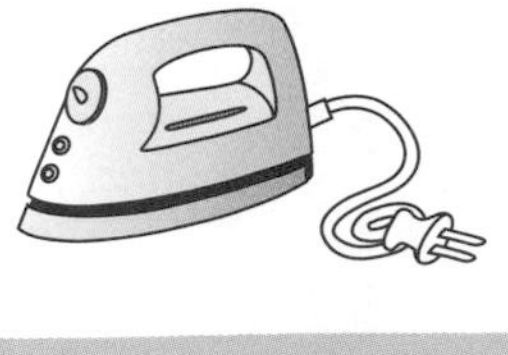

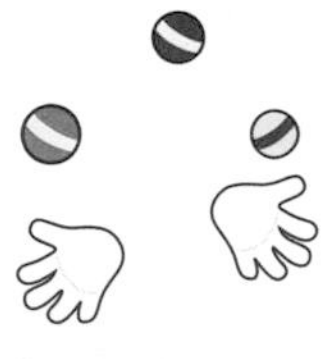

CANADA DOLLAR

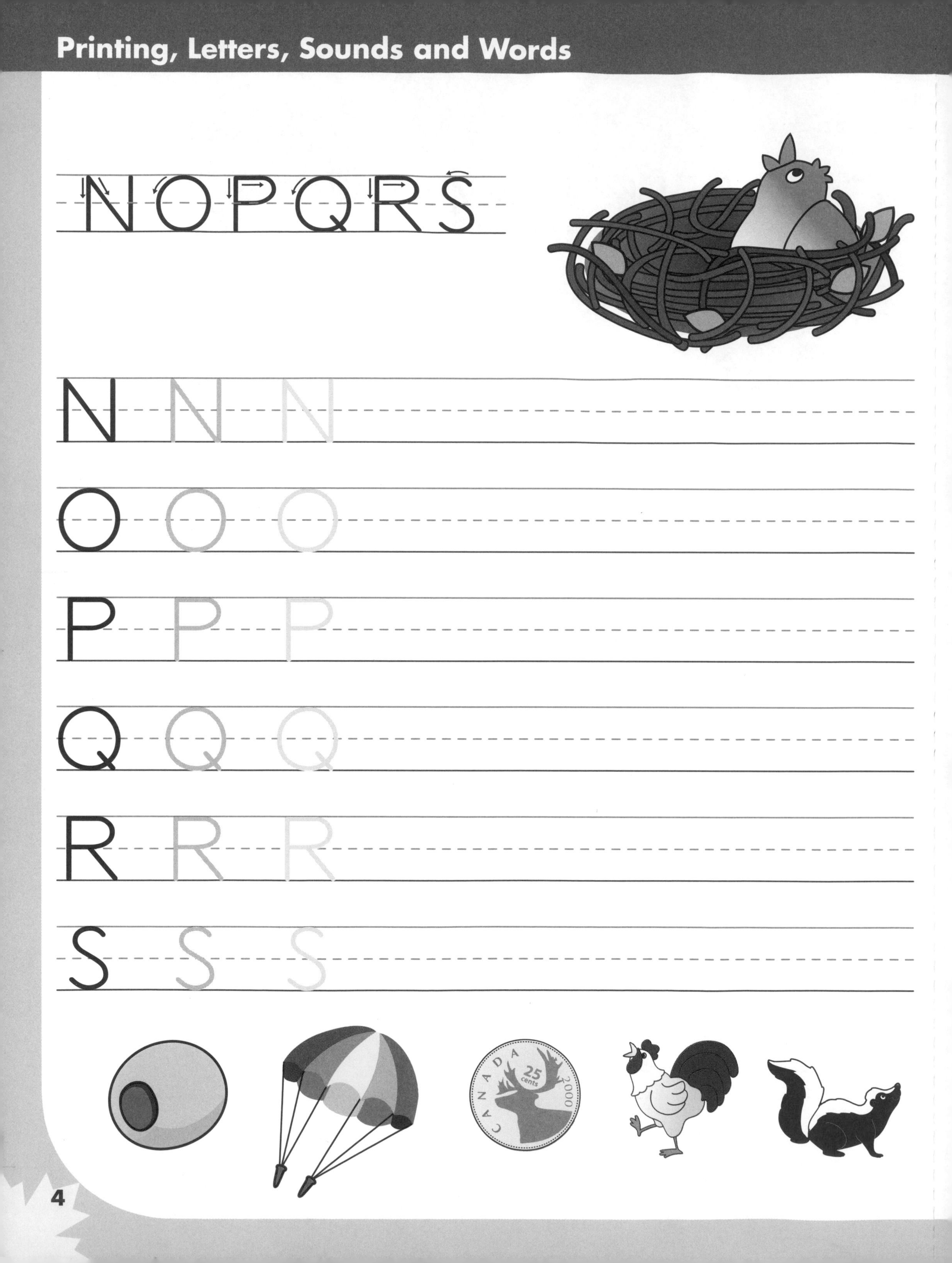
NOPQRS
N N N
O O O
P P P
Q Q Q
R R R
S S S
CANADA
25 cents
2000

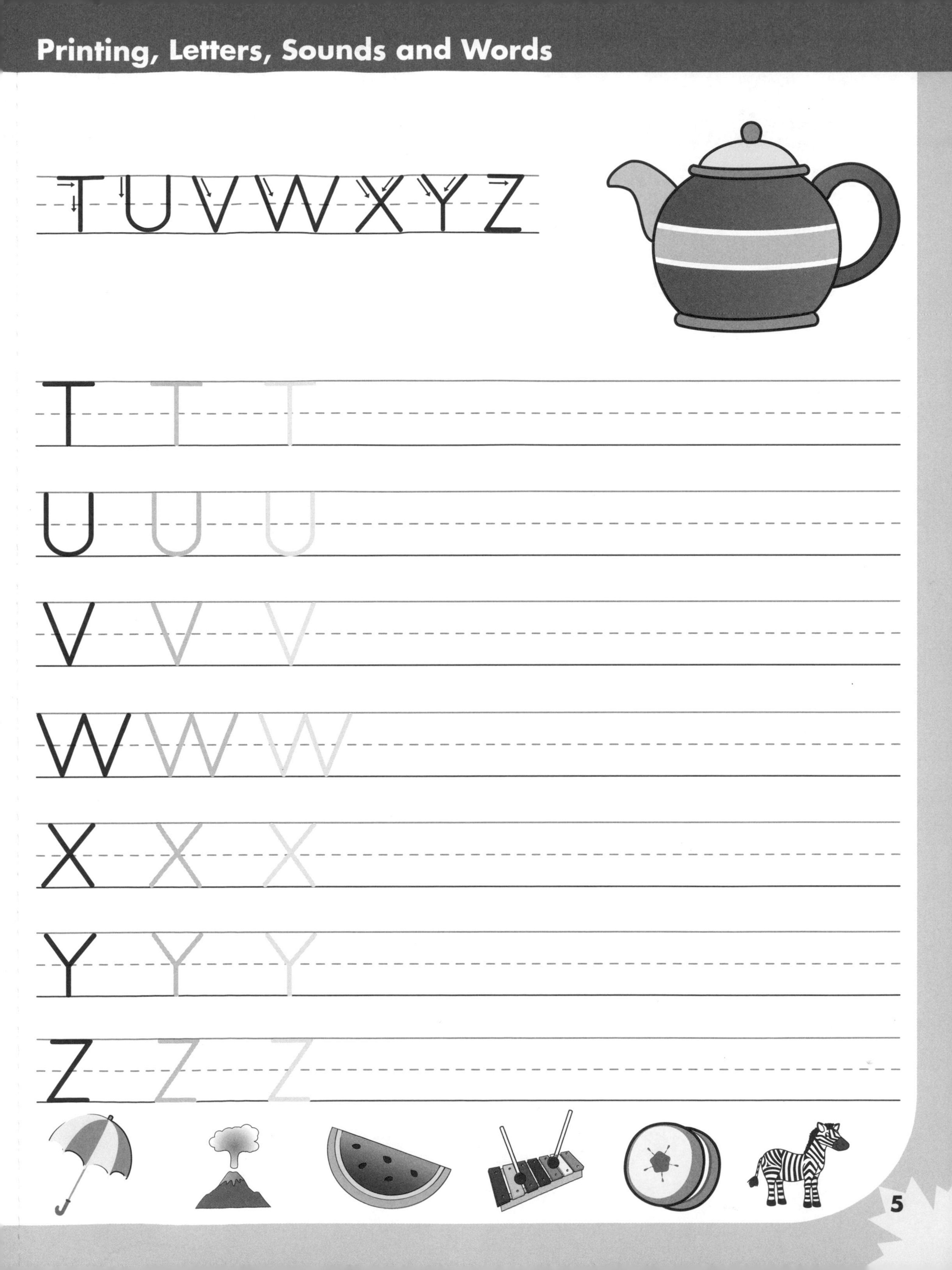
TUVWXYZ
T T T
U U U
V V V
W W W
X X X
Y Y Y
Z Z Z

Alphabetical order is when letters are put in the order of the alphabet. To put words in alphabetical order, you must look at the first letter of the words.

ABCDEFGHIJKLMNOPQRSTUVWXYZ

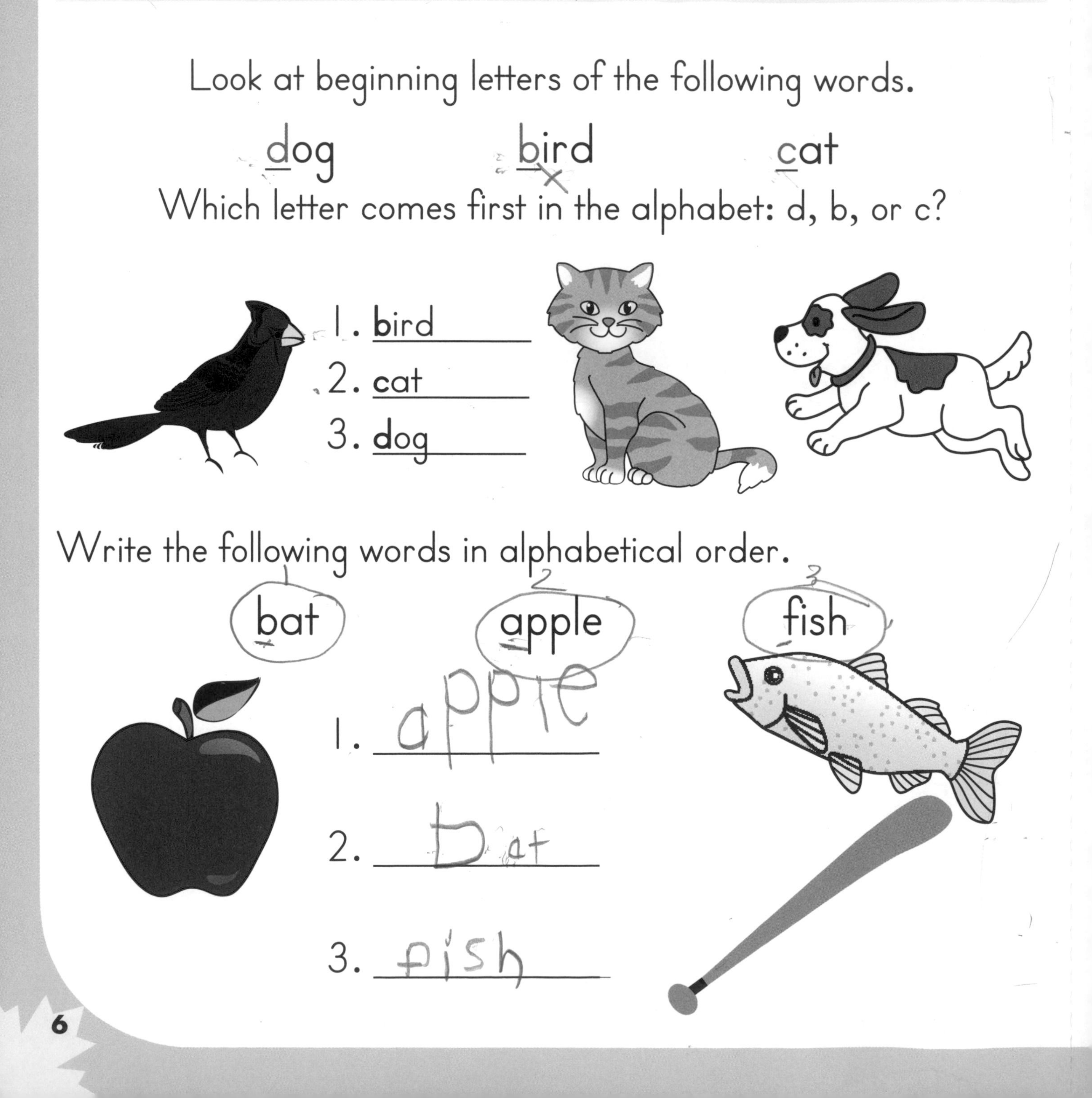

Look at beginning letters of the following words.

dog bird cat

Which letter comes first in the alphabet: d, b, or c?

1. bird
2. cat
3. dog

Write the following words in alphabetical order.

bat apple fish

1. apple
2. bat
3. fish

Alphabetical order

ABCDEFGHIJKLMNOPQRSTUVWXYZ

Look at the first letter of each word. Write the words in alphabetical order.

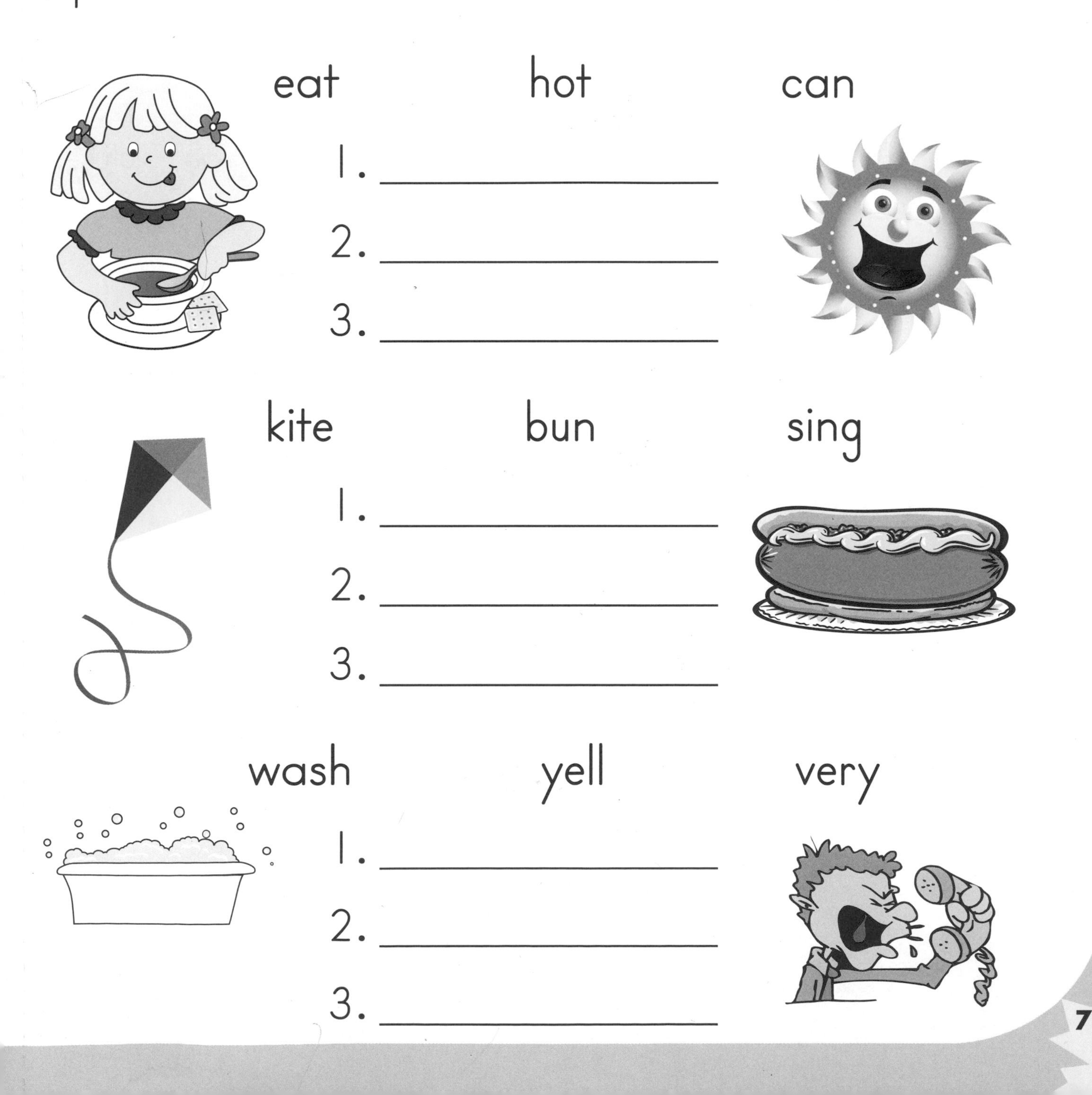

Consonants and Vowels

The following letters in the alphabet are consonants.

B C D F G H J K L M N P Q R S T V W X Y Z

The rest of the letters are vowels.

A E I O U

Beginning Consonants Bb, Cc, Dd, Ff, Gg

Look at the following pictures. Write the beginning letter for each picture.

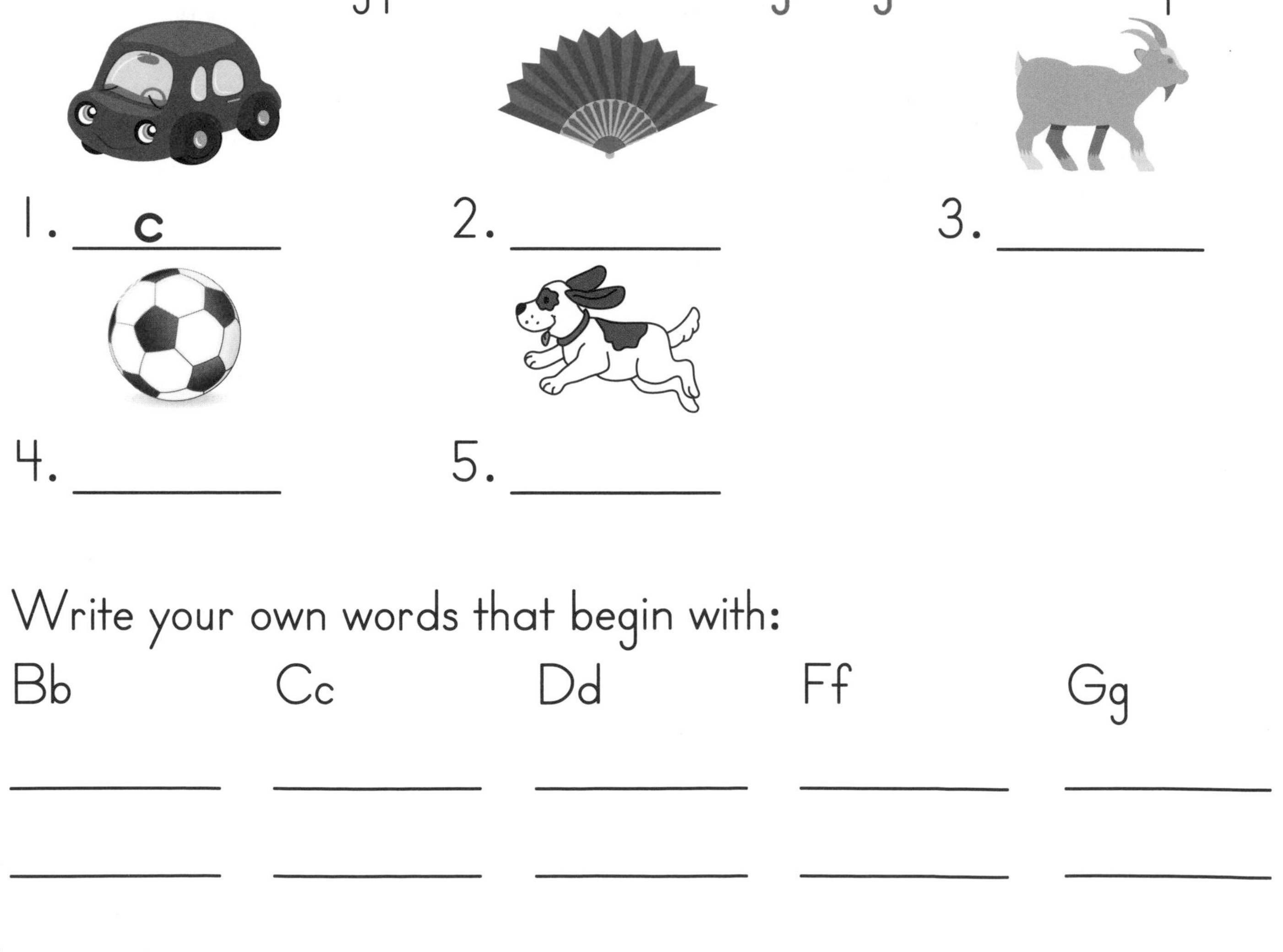

1. c
2. ________
3. ________
4. ________
5. ________

Write your own words that begin with:

Bb	Cc	Dd	Ff	Gg
________	________	________	________	________
________	________	________	________	________

Beginning Consonants Hh, Jj, Kk, Ll, Mm

Look at the following pictures. Write the beginning letter of the word for each picture.

B C D F G H J K L M N P Q R S T V W X Y Z

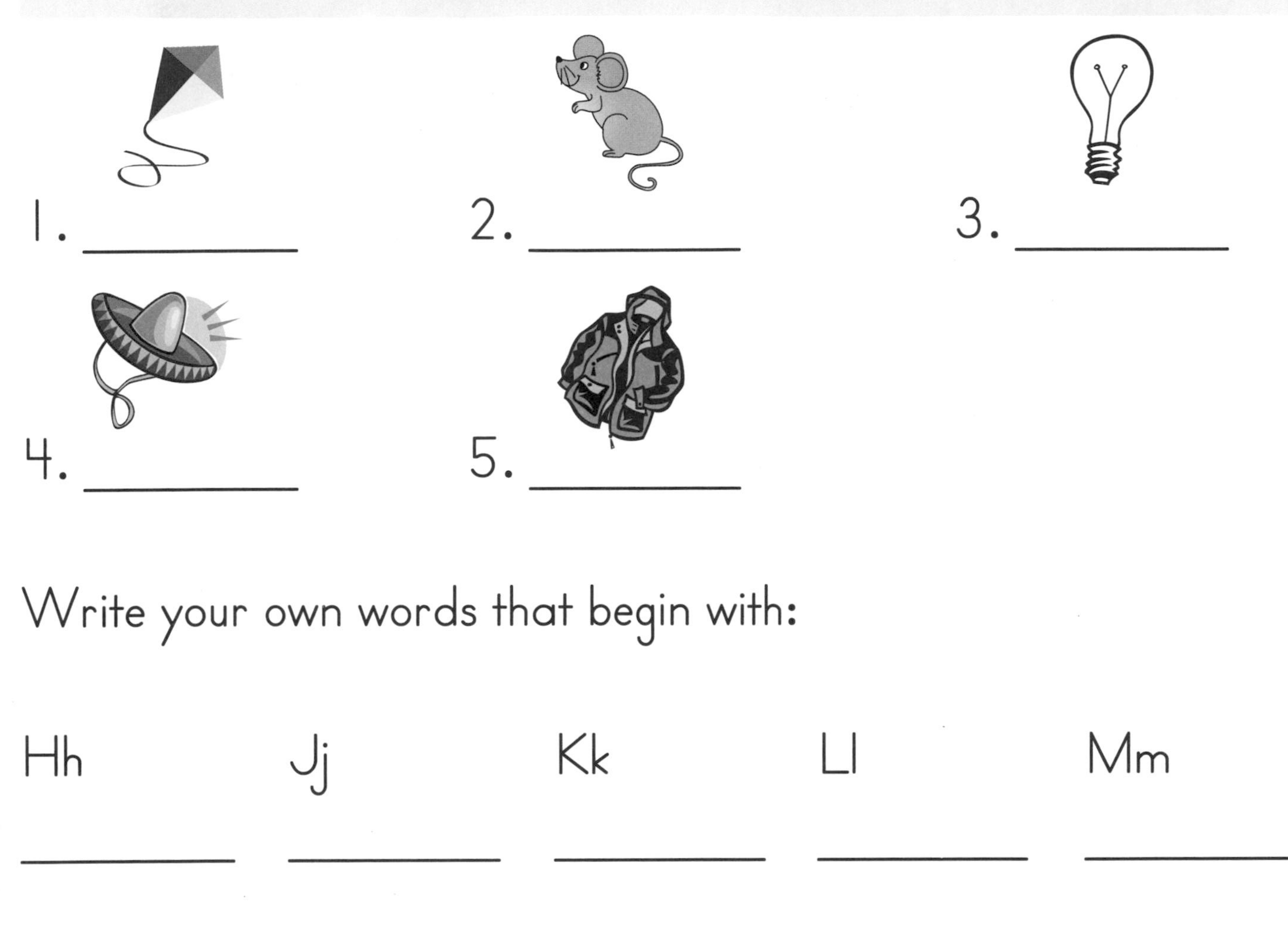

1. ________ 2. ________ 3. ________

4. ________ 5. ________

Write your own words that begin with:

Hh	Jj	Kk	Ll	Mm
________	________	________	________	________
________	________	________	________	________

Does your name begin with a consonant? Write the names of people in your family whose names begin with consonants.

____________ ____________ ____________

Beginning Consonants Nn, Pp, Qq, Rr, Ss

Look at the following pictures. Write the beginning letter of the word for each picture.

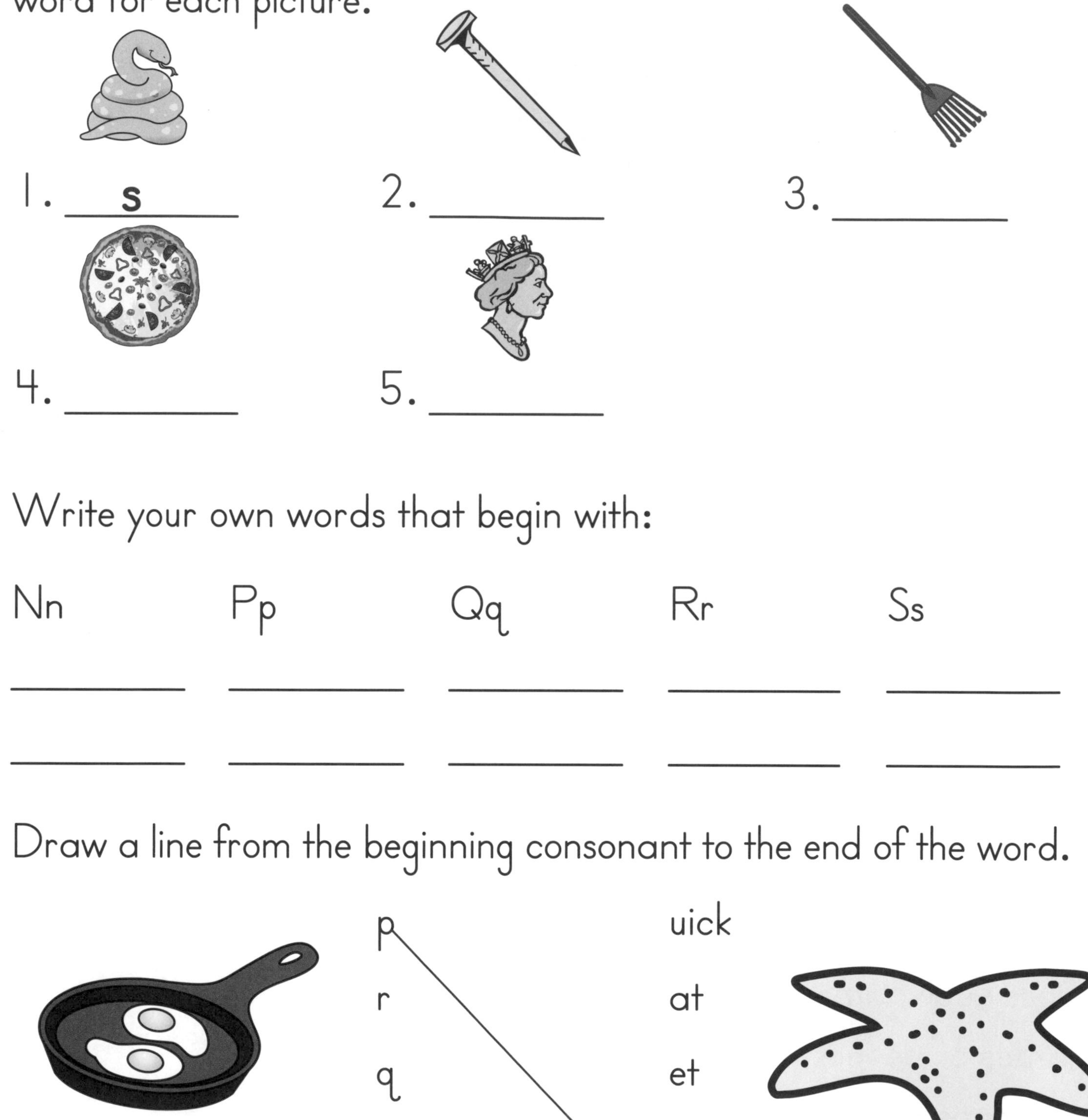

1. s
2. ________
3. ________
4. ________
5. ________

Write your own words that begin with:

Nn	Pp	Qq	Rr	Ss
________	________	________	________	________
________	________	________	________	________

Draw a line from the beginning consonant to the end of the word.

p	uick
r	at
q	et
n	and
s	an

Beginning Consonants Tt, Vv, Ww, Xx, Yy, Zz

Look at the following pictures. Write the beginning letter of the word for each picture.

1. ________ 2. ________ 3. ________

4. ________ 5. ________ 6. ________

Write your own words that begin with:

Tt	Vv	Ww	Xx	Yy	Zz
______	______	______	______	______	______
______	______	______	______	______	______

Write the missing beginning consonant for each word. Some have more than one answer.

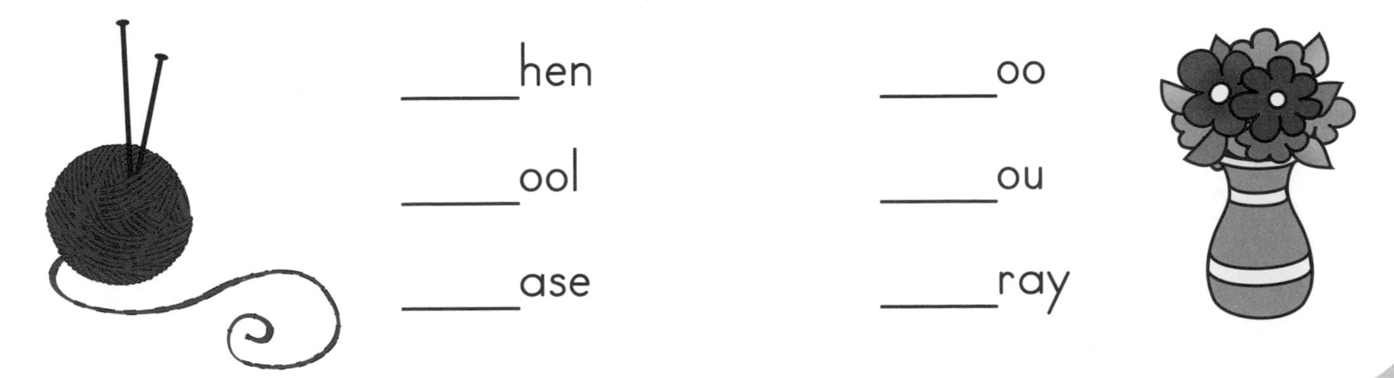

____hen ____oo

____ool ____ou

____ase ____ray

Short and Long Vowel Sounds

a e i o u

At least one vowel is found in every word.
Vowels can make short sounds or long sounds.
Long vowels sound like their letter names.

Words that have a **short a** sound.

cat	bad
last	have
fan	lamp

Think of some **short a** sound words.

Words that have a **long a** sound.

gate	made
plane	sale
fame	safe

Think of some **long a** sound words.

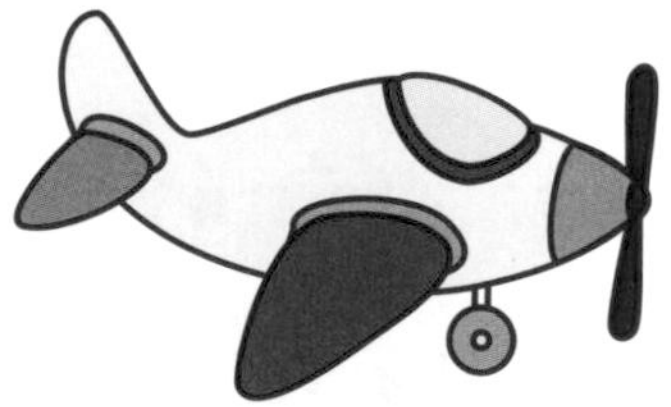

A silent e at the end of a word usually means the vowel has a long vowel sound.

SALE SALE

man mane

Short and Long Vowel Sounds

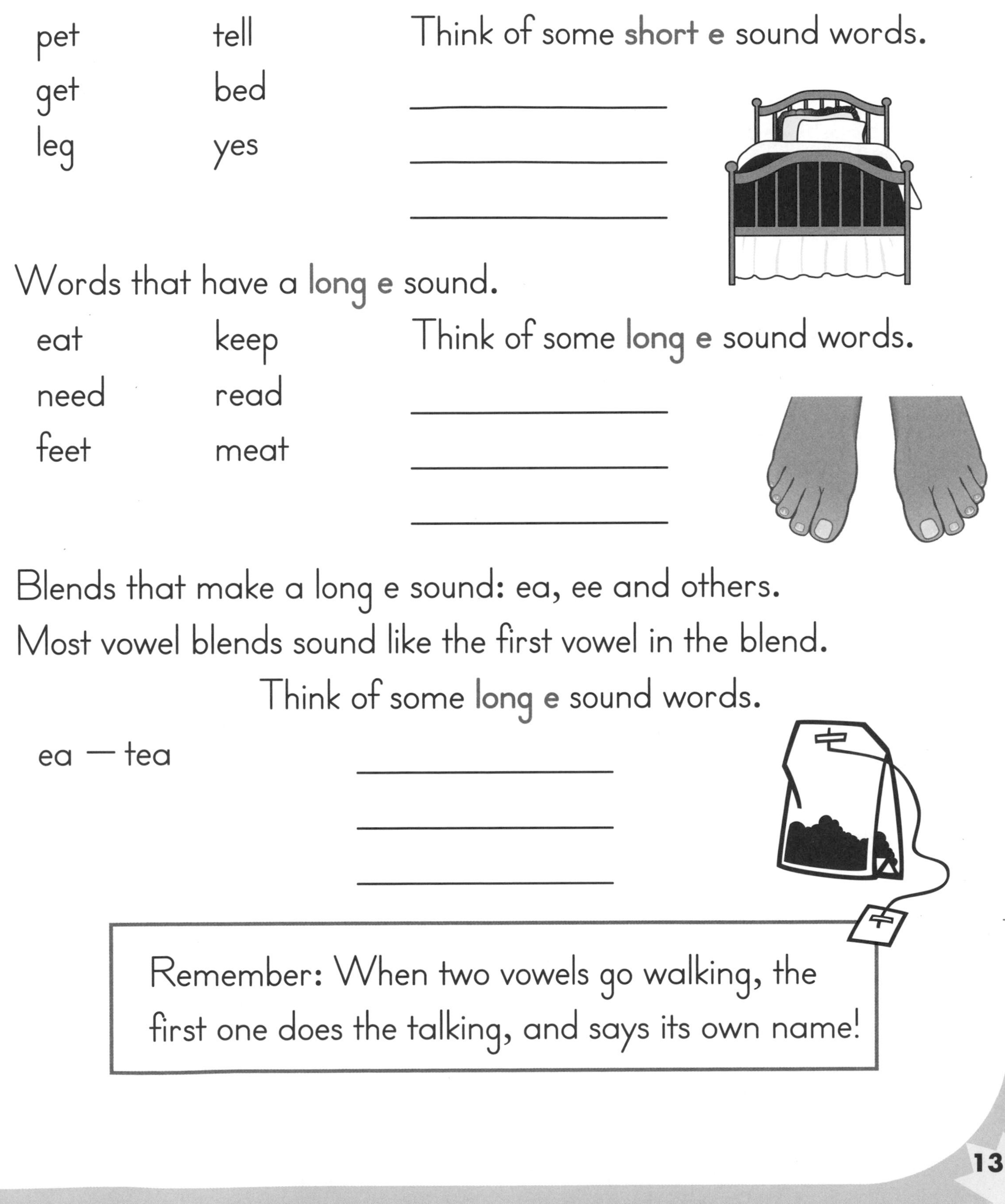

Words that have short e sound.

pet	tell
get	bed
leg	yes

Think of some short e sound words.

____

____

____

Words that have a long e sound.

eat	keep
need	read
feet	meat

Think of some long e sound words.

____

____

____

Blends that make a long e sound: ea, ee and others.

Most vowel blends sound like the first vowel in the blend.

Think of some long e sound words.

ea — tea

____

____

____

Remember: When two vowels go walking, the first one does the talking, and says its own name!

Short and Long Vowel Sounds

Words that have a **short** i sound.

sit	rip
lick	pig
fill	bin

Think of some **short** i sound words.

____

____

____

Words that have a **long** i sound.

light	bike
like	dime
bite	fine

Think of some **long** i sound words.

____

____

____

> Blend that makes **long** i sound: igh
> as in sigh, high.

Words that have a **short** o sound.

stop	dog
nob	rock
pot	doll

Think of some **short** o sound words.

____

____

____

Short and Long Vowel Sounds

Words that have long o sound.

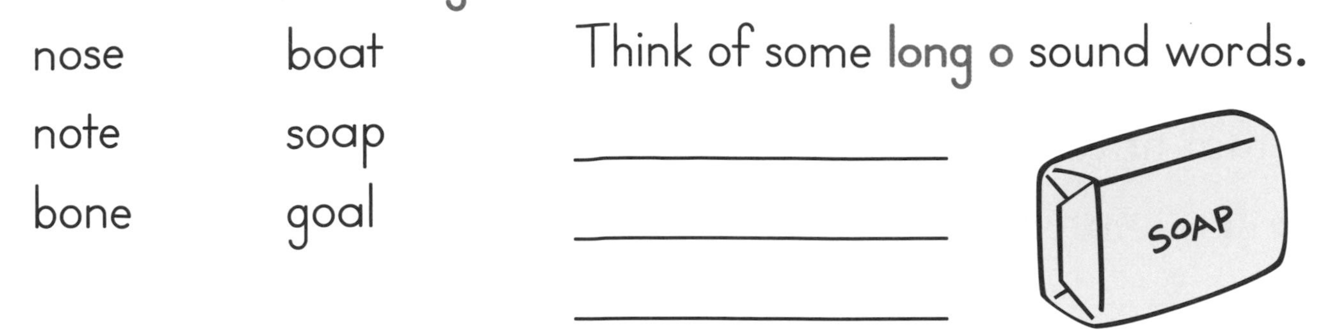

nose boat
note soap
bone goal

Think of some long o sound words.

____

____

____

Words that have short u sound.

but sun
cup fun
tub nut

Think of some short u sound words.

____

____

____

Words that have long u sound.

flute rule
huge rude
cube tune

Think of some long u sound words.

____

____

____

Tip: The oo blend also makes a long u sound: soon, food, moon

Short Vowel Sounds

Read the story below. Find some words that have **short vowel** sounds and write them below.

> Today is my birthday. I hope to have a fun day. Five friends are coming to my party. We will play pin the tail on the donkey. We will also eat cake and ice cream. I am excited to open presents. I wish for a new hockey stick.

Short Vowel Words

wish	____________	____________
____________	____________	____________
____________	____________	____________

Write a sentence using 3 of the short vowel words from above.

____

____

____

Long Vowel Sounds

Look at the invitation below.
Circle all the words that have a long vowel sound.

Halloween Party

You're invited to a costume party. Be sure to come in your favourite costume to win a prize! We will play games, make crafts and have snacks.

Time: 1:00 – 3:00
Place: 123 My Drive
When: Monday, October 30
RSVP to Peter

Tip: Vowels have a long sound when an e is added on the end of the word. pip ⇨ pipe

Write a scary Halloween sentence with 3 long vowel words in it.

____

____

____

Word Families

Word families are words that end in the same letters but begin with different letters. These are four different word families.

_ at   _ ad   _ an   _ ay

Fill in the beginning letters to make words for each of the following word families. The first one is done for you.

at	ad	an	ay
c at	___ad	___an	___ay
_ at	___ad	___an	___ay
_ at	___ad	___an	___ay
_ at	___ad	___an	___ay
_ at	___ad	___an	___ay

Words in the same family rhyme.

Word Families

et en ed ell

Look at the objects below. What are they? Fill in the missing letter for each object and draw a line from the word to the object.

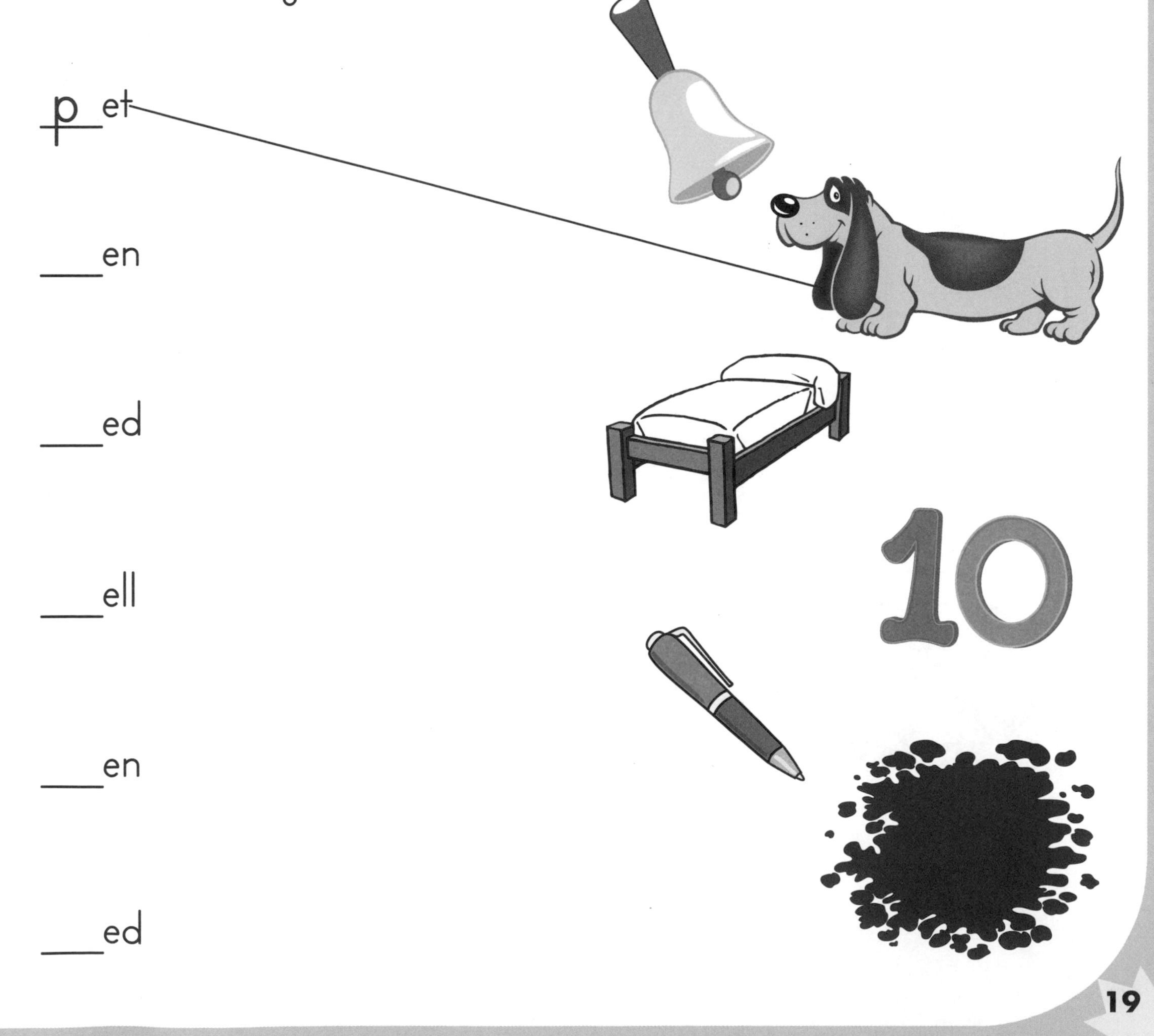

Word Families

Look at the pictures. Write the correct first letter for each object.

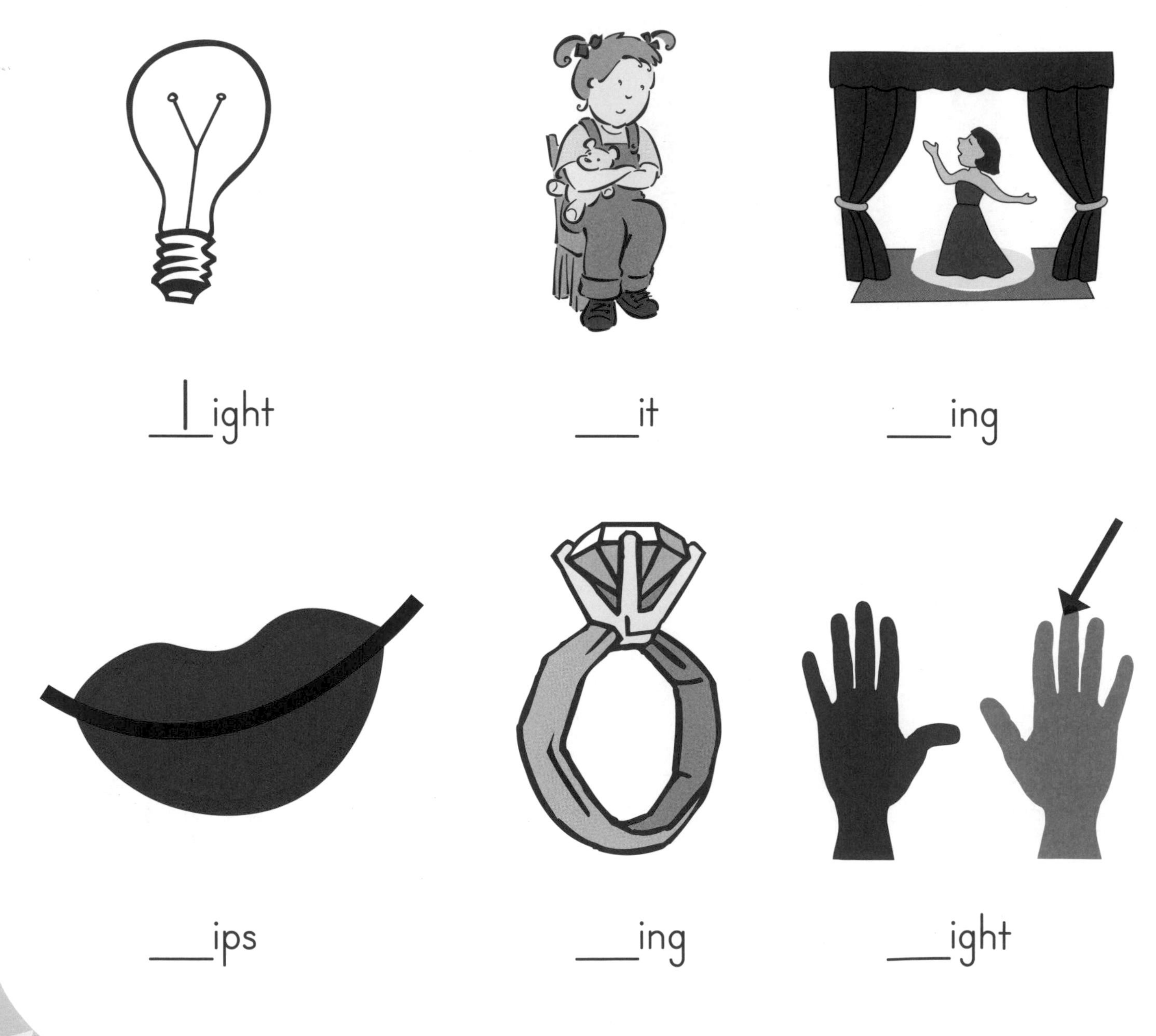

Word Families

old op ow oy

Look at the pictures. Write the correct first letter for each object.

___op ___oy ___old

___ow ___oys ___op

Word Families

ut   un   uck   unny

Look at the pictures. Write the correct first letter for each object.

___unny

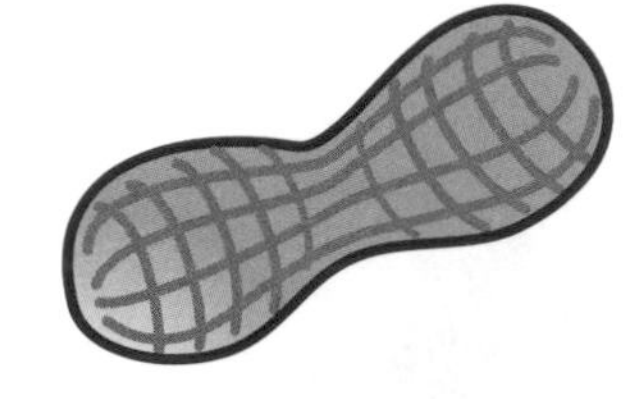

___ut

___un

___un

___uck

_uck

Blends

th

When th are together, they make one sound as in **that** or **with.**

Complete the words by adding th.

1. t h is
2. ___ ___ e
3. ___ ___ ere
4. pa ___ ___
5. ba ___ ___

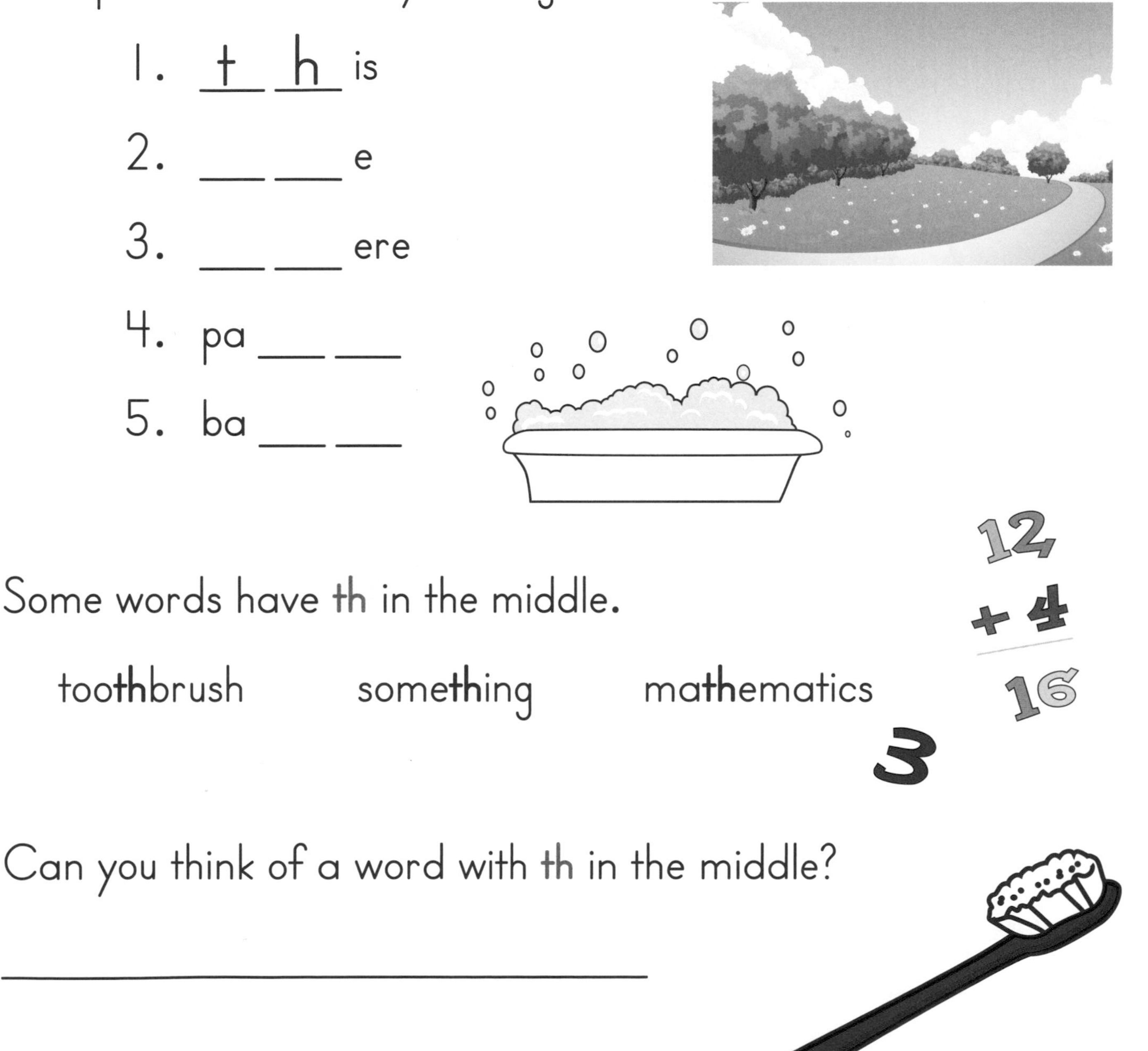

Some words have th in the middle.

too**th**brush   some**th**ing   ma**th**ematics

Can you think of a word with th in the middle?

____

Blends

sh

When **sh** are seen together, they make one sound such as in **shelf** or **wash**.

Complete the words by adding **sh**.

1. ___ ___ ape
2. fi ___ ___
3. ___ ___ ell
4. bru ___ ___
5. ___ ___ eep

Can you think of some words that begin or end with **sh**?

____

____

____

____

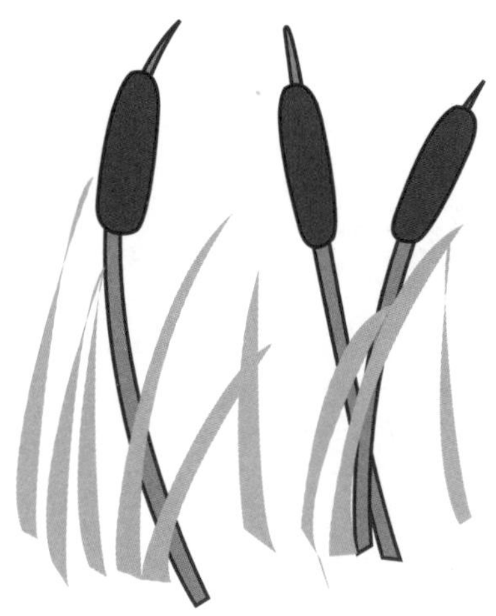

Blends

ch

When ch are seen together, they make one sound such as in cheese or such.

Complete the words by adding ch.

1. mu ___ ___
2. ___ ___ imp
3. ___ ___ at
4. ___ ___ ild
5. bea ___ ___

Look at the picture. Write all the words you can find that begin or end with ch.

____

____

Compound Words

Two words put together to make one word are compound words.
Some examples are: **sun**burn **out**side **bed**time

Look at the pictures below. Name each picture.
Put the words together to make compound words.

Compound Words

Make compound words by adding a word to each sentence. Use the list at the bottom of the page.

1. I will go to sleep tonight in my bed room______.

2. Going down the slide is fun at the play__________.

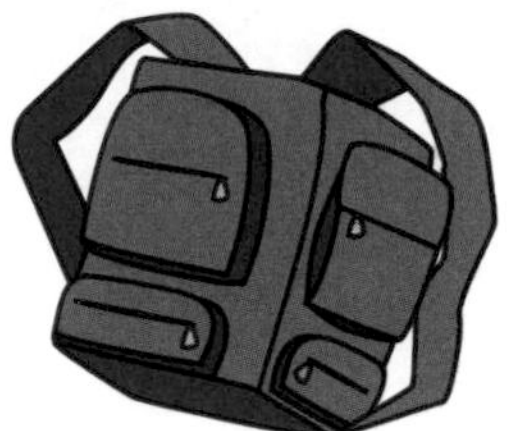

3. Most students carry a back__________.

4. The score was 5 to 3 at the base__________ game.

5. Dad built a fire in the fire__________.

Words to complete compound words:

place ground ball pack room

Prefixes

Prefixes are a part of a word that appears at the beginning of the word. Some prefixes are:

un **dis** **re** **pre**

Prefix	Meaning	Example
un	not	unhappy
dis	not	dishonest
re	again	reuse

Add **un**, **dis** or **re** to the beginning of the following words.

1. ______re______ build
2. ______________ tie

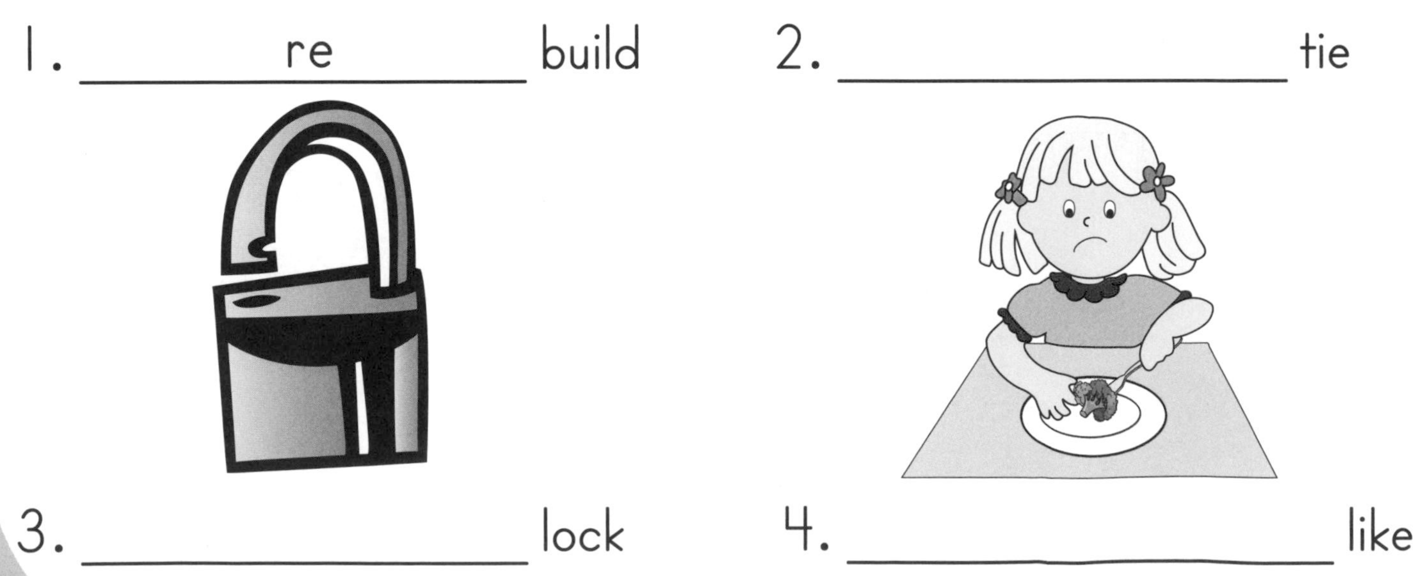

3. ______________ lock
4. ______________ like

Plural Form

You use the plural of a word when you talk about more than one of something. To make a word **plural**, you add an **s** or **es** to the end of the word.

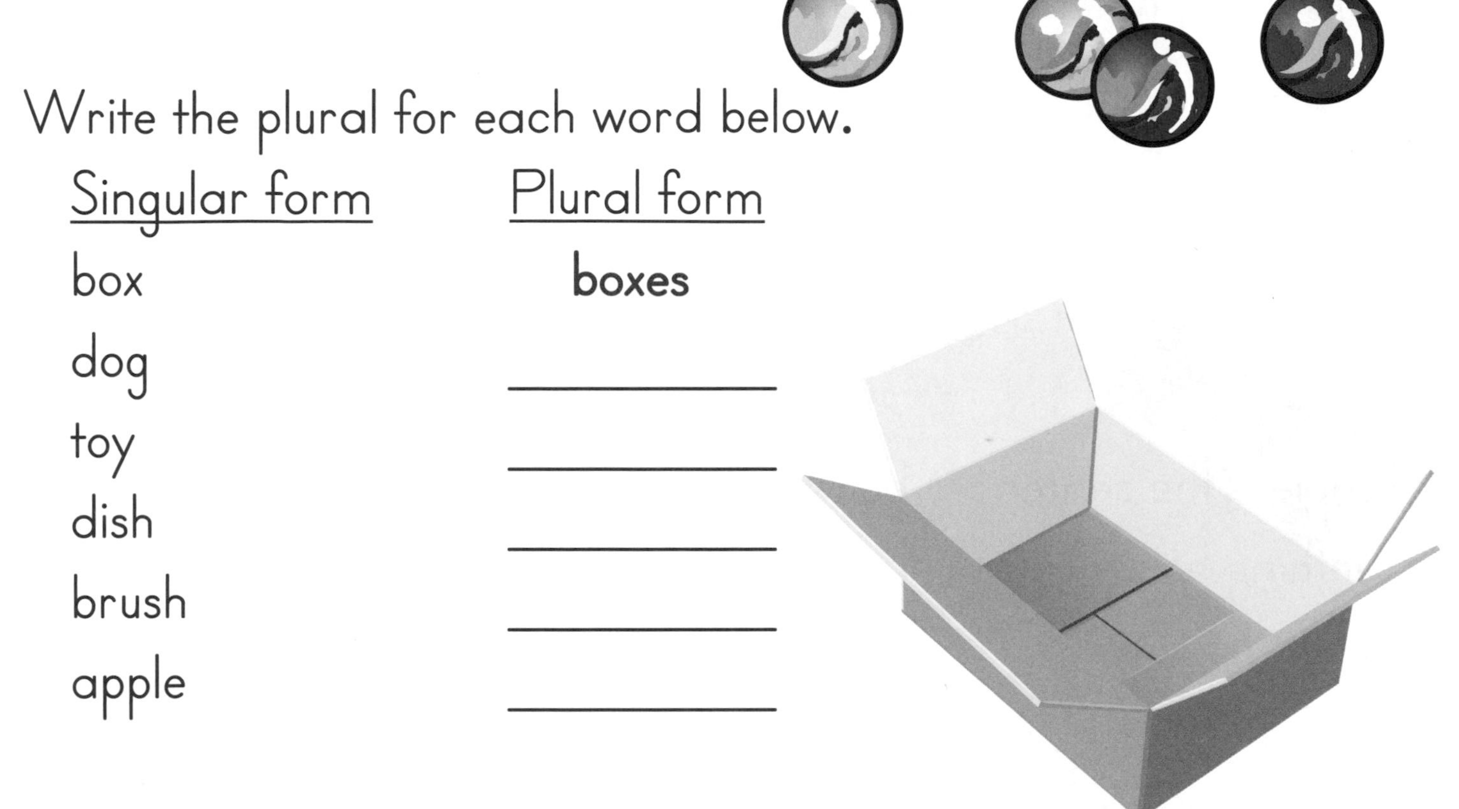

Write the plural for each word below.

Singular form	Plural form
box	**boxes**
dog	____________
toy	____________
dish	____________
brush	____________
apple	____________

Drop the y and add ies.

For some words that end in y, you have to drop the y and add ies to make them plural. Change the words below to plural.

candy	**candies**
berry	____________
bunny	____________
baby	____________

Past Tense Word Ending

ed

If something has already happened or is in the past, you add ed to the verb.

➪ Today, I will cook hotdogs.
➪ Yesterday, I cooked hotdogs.

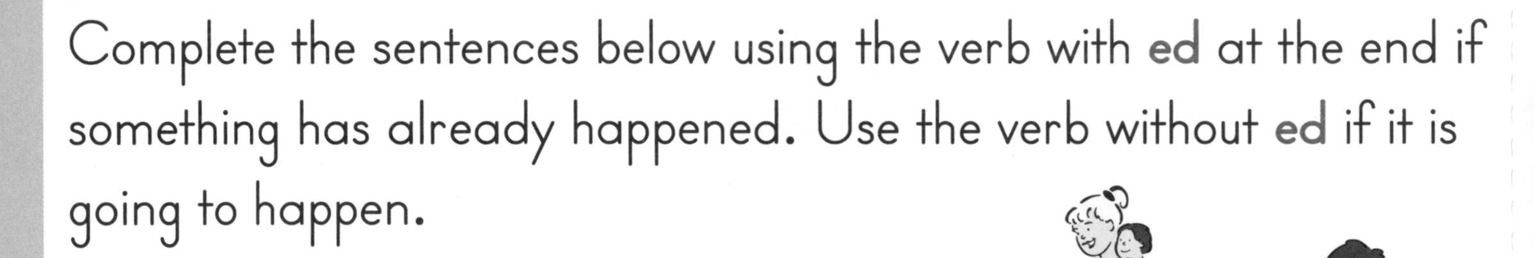

Complete the sentences below using the verb with ed at the end if something has already happened. Use the verb without ed if it is going to happen.

1. I will ____play____ with my friend.
   play or played

2. Yesterday, my mom ______________ my hair.
   wash or washed

3. Last night, I ______________ cookies to bring to school.
   bake or baked

Parts of Speech – Common Nouns

A common noun is a person, place or thing.
The words dog, pot and lake are all common nouns.

Circle the common nouns.

Noun Search

Circle the nouns in each sentence.
The first one is done.

1. The car drove very fast.

2. Most frogs are green.

3. The kids ran up the hill.

4. Dogs like to walk in the park.

5. Clowns can do magic tricks.

Parts of Speech – Common Nouns

Search for the common nouns.

Look at the picture above. Write all the common nouns you see.

____________________ ____________________

____________________ ____________________

____________________ ____________________

____________________ ____________________

Parts of Speech – Pronouns

A pronoun is another word for a person, place or thing.
Pronouns are used instead of naming a person, place or thing.
Some pronouns are: she, he, it, they, I, us, me.

Using the following pronouns, complete the sentences.

we us me I he she it they

1. She had fun at the party.

2. Sammy played with ______ yesterday.

3. ______ got an A on my math test.

4. ______ took their hockey sticks to the park.

PARTY!

Write your own sentence using a pronoun.

____

____

Parts of Speech – Pronouns

Replace the common nouns with pronouns.
Use the following pronouns:

he she it they

Remember common nouns are people, places or things.

1. The students went to the park.
   They went to the park.

2. My friend loves cookies.
   ____________ loves cookies.

3. The ball bounces very high.
   ____________ bounces very high.

4. The girl laughed at the cartoon.
   ____________ laughed at the cartoon.

Parts of Speech – Proper Nouns

Proper nouns are names given to specific people or places. They always begin with a capital letter.

Your name is a proper noun.
What is your name? ______________________________

The name of your school is a proper noun.
What is the name of your school? ______________________________

The name of the city you live in is a proper noun.
What city do you live in? ______________________________

Canada is a proper noun as it is the name of a country.

Circle the proper nouns.

Beth loves math class. She knows how to count to 100. She goes to Maple Public School. She has two best friends who play ball with her. Their names are Lilly and Emily. Beth lives on Lake Street in a yellow house.

Parts of Speech – Adjectives

Adjectives describe people, places or things.

happy boy	big hat
red mittens	soft kitten
one crayon	small dog

Silly Sentences

Choose adjectives from below or choose your own to make silly sentences.

1. The clown has ____________ feet and a ____________ nose.
2. At the party, we ate ____________ cake and played ____________ games.
3. My mommy read me a ____________ book with ____________ pictures.

Adjectives

delicious	fun	amazing	huge
yucky	silly	colourful	noisy
red	crazy	sad	funny
big	good	scary	happy

Parts of Speech – Verbs

Verbs are action words.

Run, play, jump, go, and do are all verbs.

Read each sentence and circle the verbs. The first one is done.

1. The dog (ran) after the ball.
2. We swim on very hot days.
3. After we swim, we eat ice cream.
4. In the spring, children ride their bikes.

Look at the pictures. Use a verb to describe it.

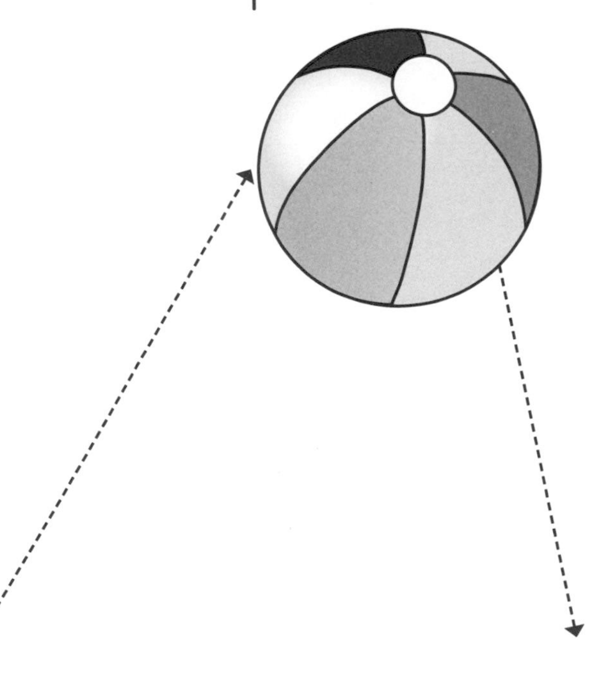

______________________ ______________________

Parts of Speech – Verbs

Complete the story with verbs.
Write verbs into the story from the list below.

Thanksgiving

Thanksgiving is a special celebration. It is a celebration to give thanks for a good harvest and other good fortune over the past year. Many families ____travel____ to see each other at this time of year. Thanksgiving is in October. People often ________________ turkey for Thanksgiving dinner and ________________ pumpkin pie for dessert. During dinner, families may ________________ about what they are thankful for. Around Thanksgiving, leaves ________________ from the trees. Some children might ________________ in the leaves for fun. Others may ________________ outside before the cold weather begins.

Verbs to use:

	cook	play	~~travel~~
fall	talk	jump	eat

Draw a line through each verb as you use it to make sure you use all of them.

Parts of Speech – Adverbs

Adverbs are words that describe action words or verbs. They describe how, when, where, or how much about a verb.

Sally ran quickly. *How?*

I am going swimming now. *When?*

Please come here. *Where?*

My dad yelled a lot when he hit his finger with a hammer. *How much?*

Use an adverb to describe the verb in the following sentences. Circle the verb.

The cat purred loudly.

My family went for a walk ________________.

He ran __________.

I rode my bike ________________.

Adverbs:

loudly	yesterday	quickly	school
quietly	today	slowly	home
away			

Capital Letters

We use capital letters in different ways:

1. The first word of every sentence begins with a capital letter.
   ➪ My dog loves to run.
2. The word I always uses a capital letter.
   ➪ You and I can be friends.
3. Specific names of people and places always begin with a capital letter.
   ➪ My friends' names are Nick, Lia, and Fred.
4. Titles of books, movies, and T.V. shows begin with capital letters.
   ➪ Have you read The Space Race?

Circle the letters that should be capitals in each sentence.

1. my friend charlie is in my class.
2. i live on lake street in edmonton, alberta, canada.
3. our dog tippy loves to run after balls.
4. the teacher's name is mrs. anderson.

Put the word I in each sentence.

1. ____ am happy to see you.
2. ____ can't wait for summer vacation.
3. My brother and ____ love to play games.
4. Even though you and ____ want the same cookie, will you give it to me, please?

Sentence Punctuation

. ? !

All sentences start with a capital letter. A telling sentence ends with a period. ➪ You are my friend.

An exciting telling sentence ends with an exclamation mark!

➪ I won a prize!

A question ends with a question mark?

➪ Are you going to the park?

Put a ., ?, or a ! at the end of each sentence.

1. Our country is called Canada_._
2. What is the name of your city___
3. My sister's name is Michelle___
4. My birthday is today___
5. When are you coming to my house___
6. The score was close but our soccer team won the game___

Synonyms

Synonyms are words that mean the same thing.
Big and large are synonyms.

Choose the Synonym

Read the first word. Circle another word that is a synonym.
The first one is done.

fast	slow	run	quick
happy	shy	glad	sad
laugh	funny	cry	chuckle
skinny	thin	fat	small
tiny	large	big	small
shy	courage	happy	bashful
scared	silly	afraid	Halloween

Synonym Word Search

ANGRY	FAST	MAD	RUG
BIG	FRIEND	PAL	SMALL
CARPET	LARGE	QUICK	TINY

Antonyms

Antonyms are words that mean the opposite of each other. Fast and slow are antonyms.

Finding Antonyms

Draw a line to connect antonyms.

add	small
before	courageous
happy	short
big	down
scared	in
up	subtract
out	sad
tall	after

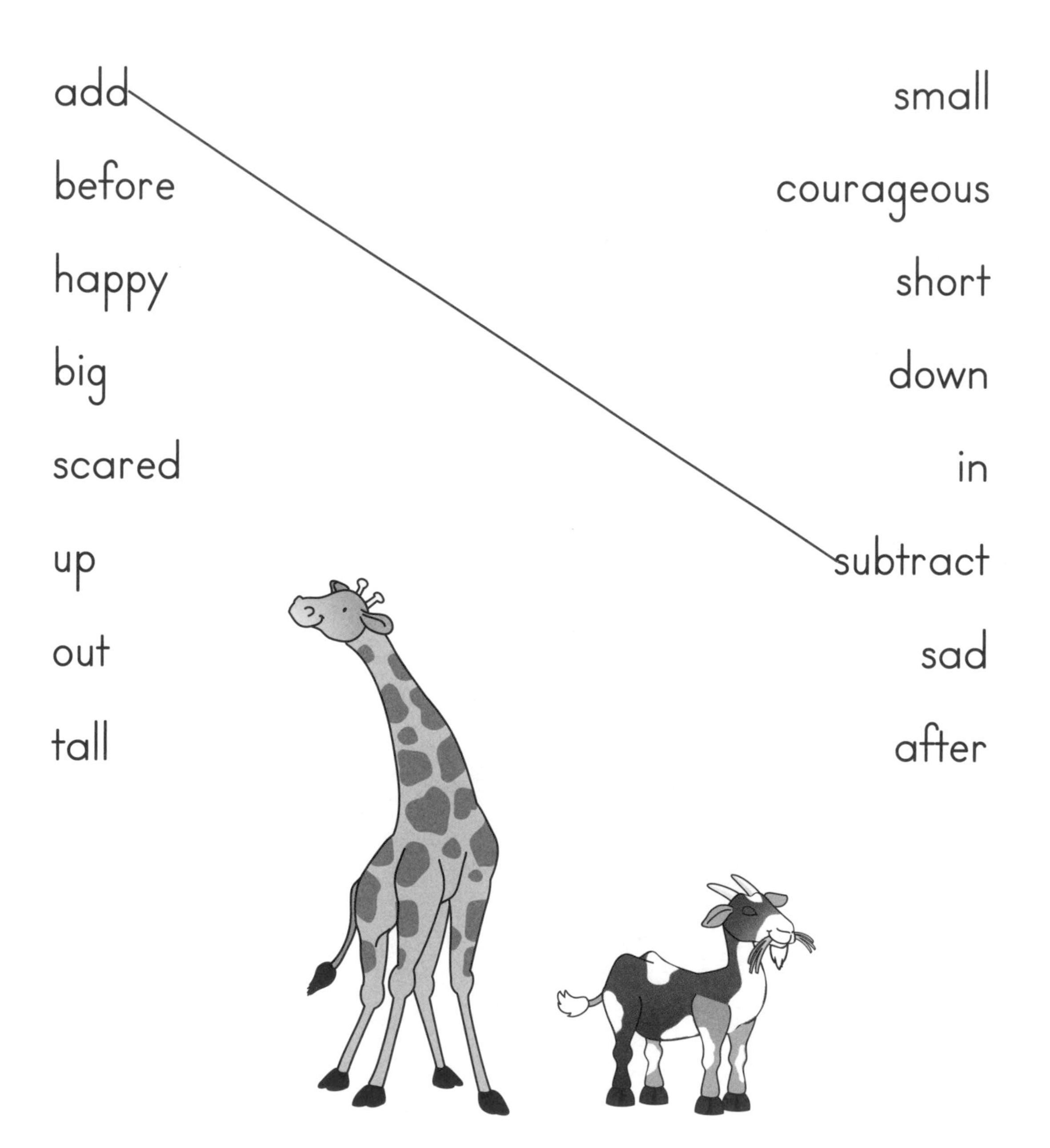

Antonym Crossword Puzzle

Solve the puzzle by finding the antonym for each clue.
Print the antonym in the puzzle.

ACROSS

2. windy
4. laugh
6. loud

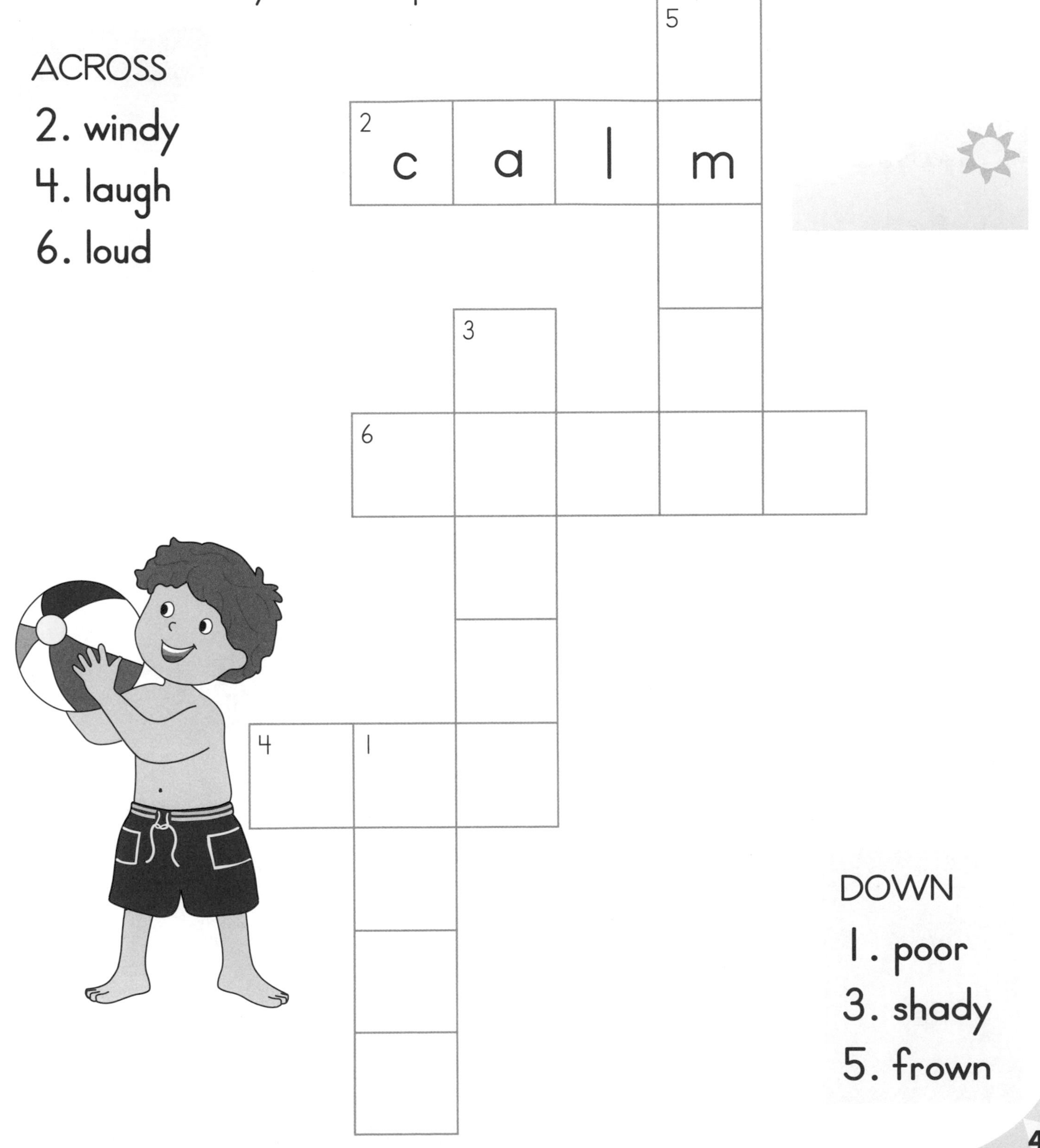

DOWN

1. poor
3. shady
5. frown

Words to Know

You should know how to spell these words.
You will use them when you write.

always
before
call
fast
gave
made
pull
sit
these
use
why
write

around
best
cold
first
goes
many
read
sleep
those
very
wish

your
because
both
does
five
green
off
right
tell
upon
wash

work
been
don't
found
its
or
sing
their
us
which
would

Words to Know

Look at the following words. Practice spelling them. Ask someone to read the words aloud to you to make sure you can spell them.

always before call fast

gave made pull sit these

use why write around best

Words to Know

Continue to practice.

cold first goes many read

sleep those very wish your

because both does five green

Words to Know

Continue to practice.

off right tell upon wash

work been buy don't found

its or sing their us

which would

Canada Day – Brainstorming

Canada Day is on July 1st and it celebrates Canada's birthday. Many Canadians celebrate Canada Day with family and friends. Some go to parties and watch fireworks to celebrate.

How do you celebrate Canada Day? Brainstorm about things you do or would like to do to celebrate Canada Day. Print your ideas in the circles.

Writing about Canada Day

Use your ideas from the previous page to write about your Canada Day celebration. Use at least 5 verbs (action words) and 3 adverbs (to describe verbs) in your writing. Some examples of verbs and adverbs are below.

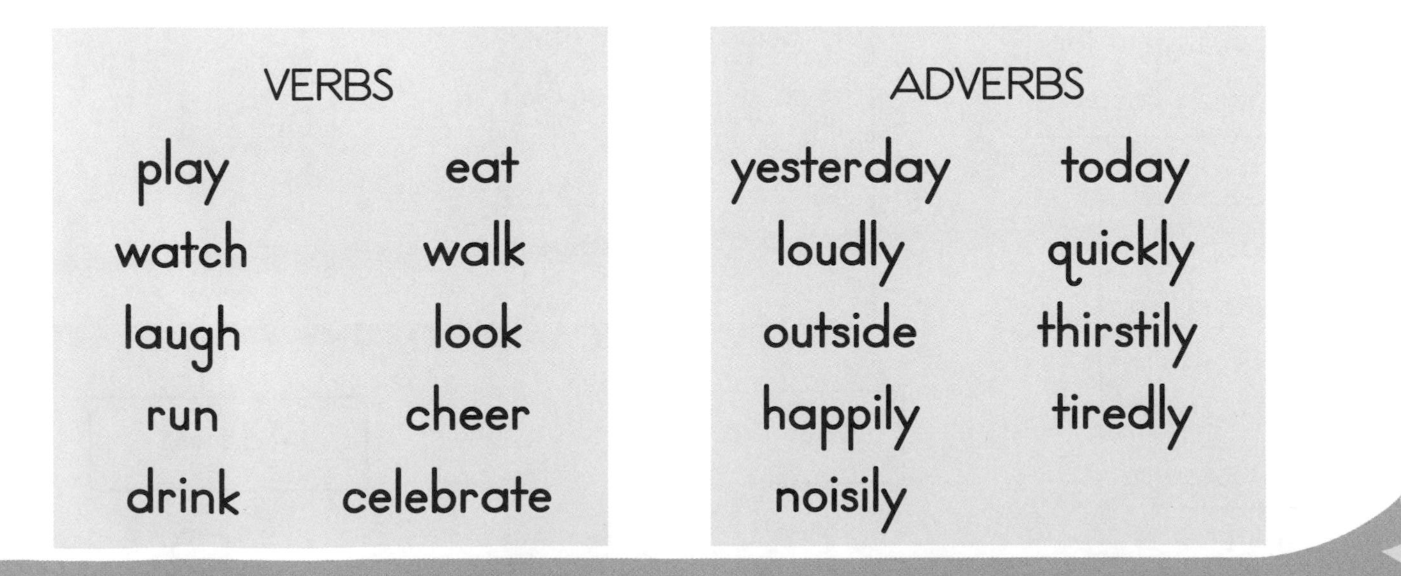

Postcards

A postcard has a picture on one side and a short note on the other. You might send a postcard when you go on a trip.

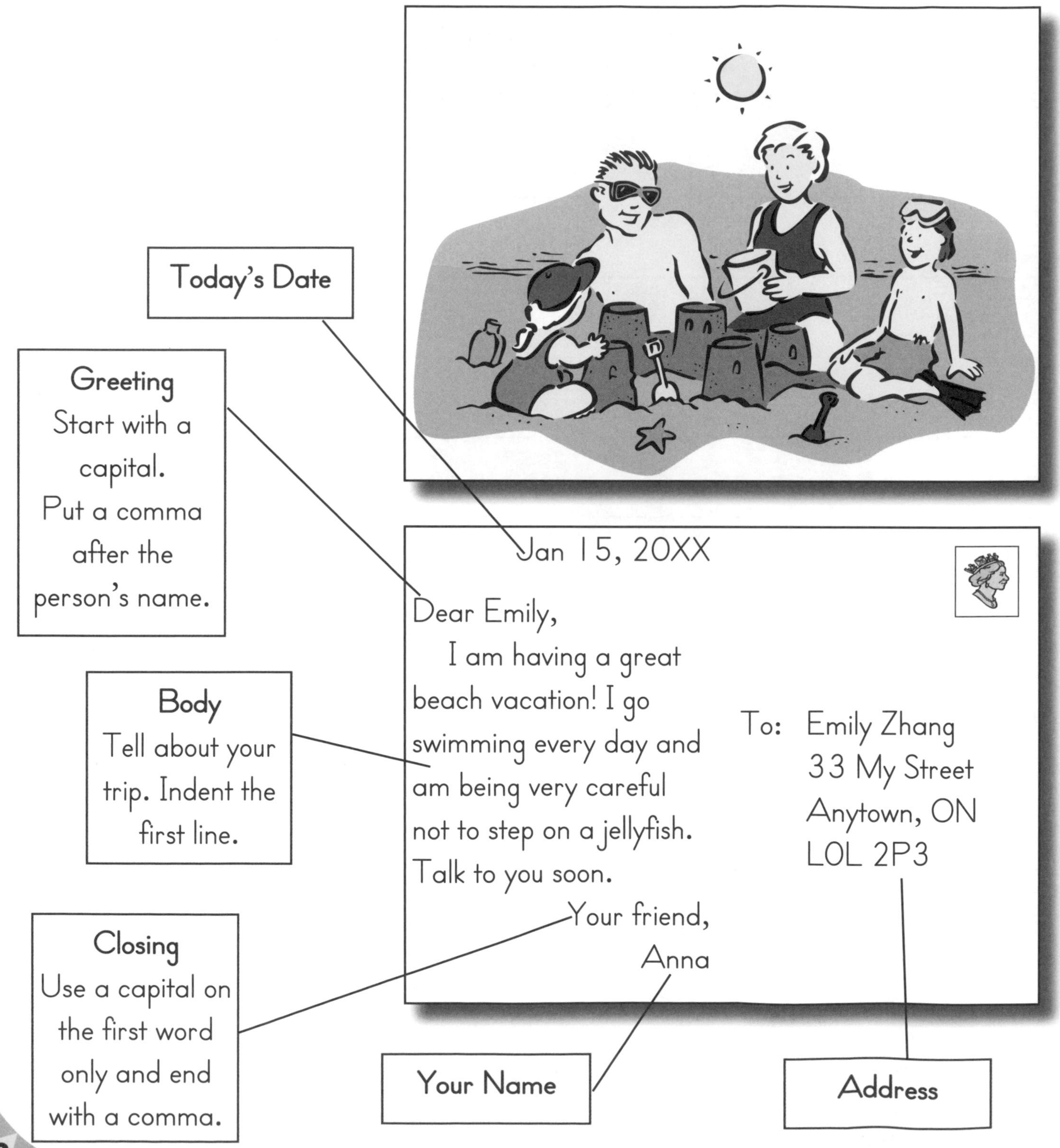

Write Your Own Postcard

Write a postcard to someone about a trip you have been on or would like to go on. Then draw a picture on the front.

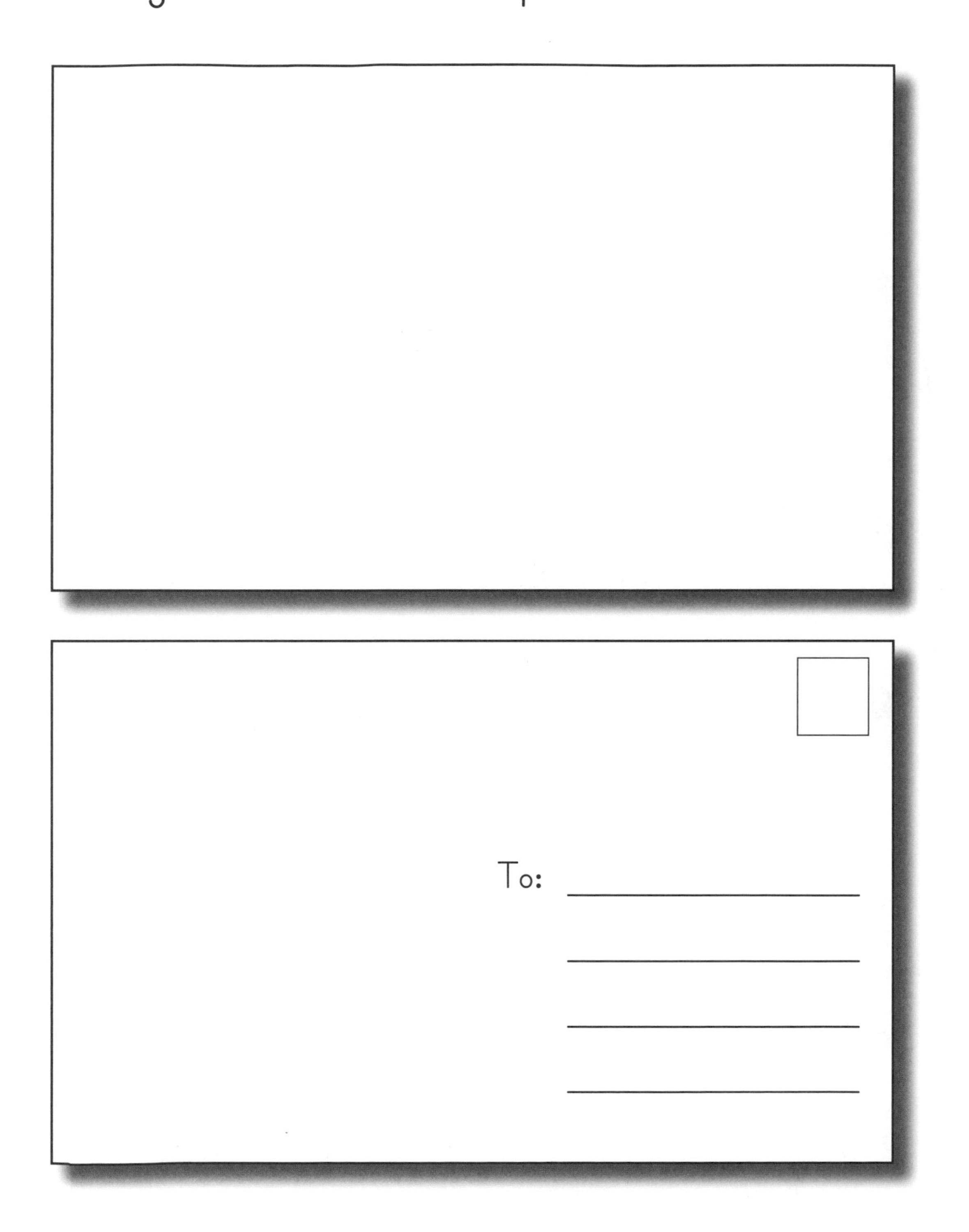

Narrative

A narrative tells a story that may or may not be based of facts.

Parts of a Narrative

Setting: Who, When, Where
Events: Parts of the story that lead to a problem
Problem: What needs to be resolved
Resolution: How the problem is solved

Mrs. Smith's Circus Trip

Mrs. Smith's Grade 2 class was going to go on a trip to the circus. Everyone was very excited about it. To go on the trip, the entire class had to finish their homework every day for one week. There were fifteen students in the class and most finished their homework every day. There was only one boy who did not always finish his homework. His name was Jesse.

Mrs. Smith checked homework every day. The students were very nervous about the homework check....

Narrative

Look at Mrs. Smith's Circus Trip from the previous page.

Setting: Mrs. Smith's classroom
Mrs. Smith
14 students, Jesse

Events:
1. Mrs. Smith's class found out about a circus trip they may be able to go on.
2. They can go on the trip only if everyone finishes their homework.
3. Mrs. Smith checks homework every day.

Problem: Jesse does not always finish his homework.

Think about a way to continue the story with your own words. First decide what the next events will be. Then determine what the resolution will be. Will Mrs. Smith's class go to the circus?

Events	Resolution
______________________	______________________
______________________	______________________
______________________	______________________

Narrative Mrs. Smith's Circus Trip

Now, finish the story with the events and resolution that you completed on the previous page.

Couplet Poetry

A couplet is a poem with two lines that rhyme.

> I have a funny, furry cat
> Who licks his fur while wearing a hat.

Think of some of your own rhyming words.

______	______	______
______	______	______
______	______	______
______	______	______

Write Your Own Couplet

Use some words from the previous page to create your own couplet. Draw a picture to go with your couplet.

Book Covers

Book covers are designed to attract readers and make them to want to read the book. The book cover should include the title of the book, the author's name and a picture that shows what the book is about.

Design a book cover for **Mrs. Smith's Circus Trip.**

Solutions

Printing, Letters, Sounds and Words

Alphabetical order is when letters are put in the order of the alphabet. To put words in alphabetical order, you must look at the first letter of the words.

ABCDEFGHIJKLMNOPQRSTUVWXYZ

Look at beginning letters of the following words.

dog bird cat

Which letter comes first in the alphabet: d, b, or c?

1. bird
2. cat
3. dog

Write the following words in alphabetical order.

bat apple fish

1. apple
2. bat
3. fish

6

Page 6

Printing, Letters, Sounds and Words

Alphabetical order

ABCDEFGHIJKLMNOPQRSTUVWXYZ

Look at the first letter of each word. Write the words in alphabetical order.

eat hot can
1. can
2. eat
3. hot

kite bun sing
1. bun
2. kite
3. sing

wash yell very
1. very
2. wash
3. yell

7

Page 7

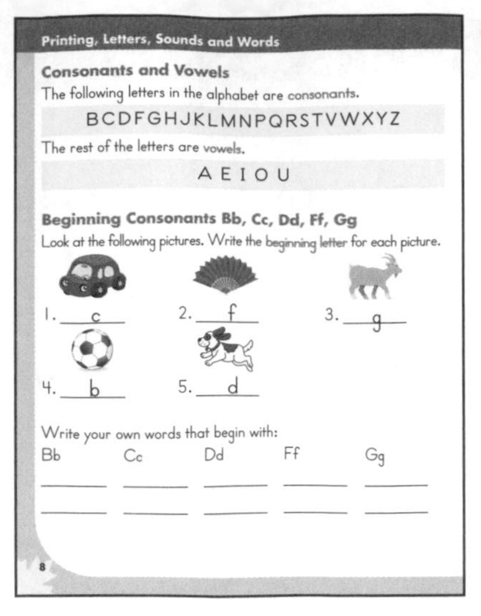
Printing, Letters, Sounds and Words

Consonants and Vowels

The following letters in the alphabet are consonants.

BCDFGHJKLMNPQRSTVWXYZ

The rest of the letters are vowels.

A E I O U

Beginning Consonants Bb, Cc, Dd, Ff, Gg

Look at the following pictures. Write the beginning letter for each picture.

1. c 2. f 3. g
4. b 5. d

Write your own words that begin with:

Bb Cc Dd Ff Gg

8

Page 8

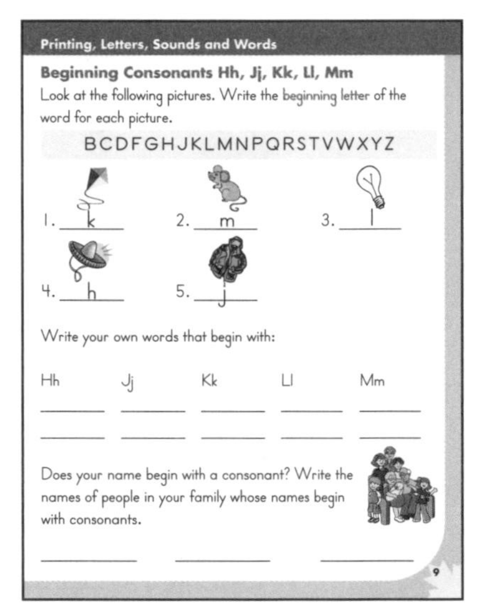
Printing, Letters, Sounds and Words

Beginning Consonants Hh, Jj, Kk, Ll, Mm

Look at the following pictures. Write the beginning letter of the word for each picture.

BCDFGHJKLMNPQRSTVWXYZ

1. k 2. m 3. l
4. h 5. j

Write your own words that begin with:

Hh Jj Kk Ll Mm

Does your name begin with a consonant? Write the names of people in your family whose names begin with consonants.

9

Page 9

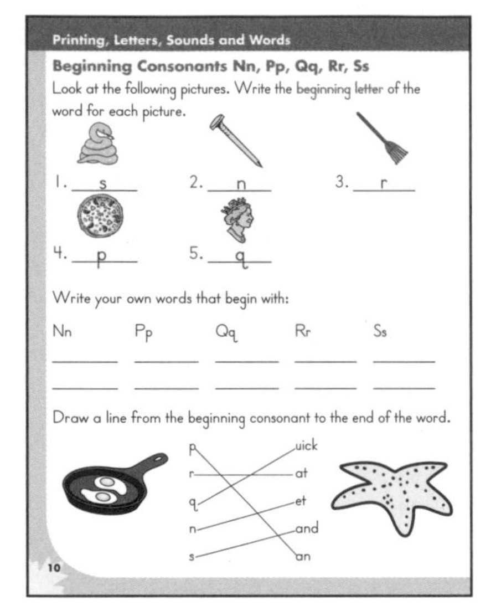
Printing, Letters, Sounds and Words

Beginning Consonants Nn, Pp, Qq, Rr, Ss

Look at the following pictures. Write the beginning letter of the word for each picture.

1. s 2. n 3. r
4. p 5. q

Write your own words that begin with:

Nn Pp Qq Rr Ss

Draw a line from the beginning consonant to the end of the word.

p uick
r at
q et
n and
s an

10

Page 10

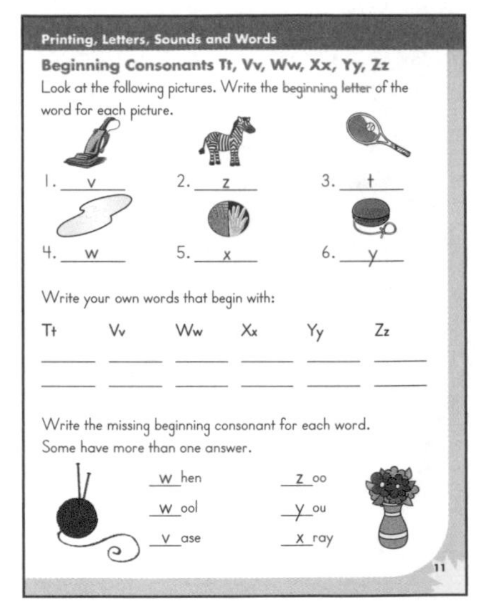
Printing, Letters, Sounds and Words

Beginning Consonants Tt, Vv, Ww, Xx, Yy, Zz

Look at the following pictures. Write the beginning letter of the word for each picture.

1. v 2. z 3. t
4. w 5. x 6. y

Write your own words that begin with:

Tt Vv Ww Xx Yy Zz

Write the missing beginning consonant for each word. Some have more than one answer.

w hen z oo
w ool y ou
v ase x ray

11

Page 11

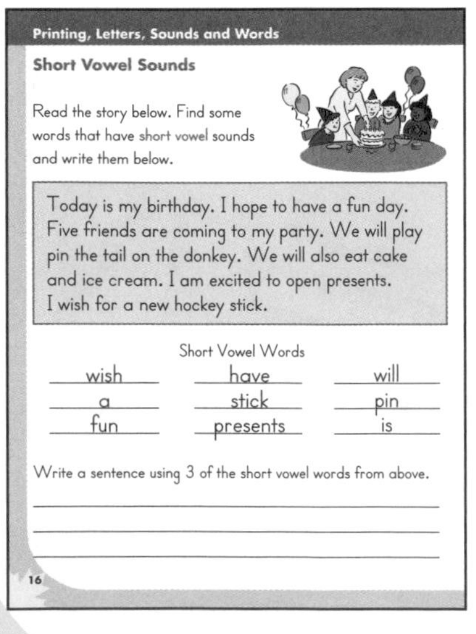
Printing, Letters, Sounds and Words

Short Vowel Sounds

Read the story below. Find some words that have short vowel sounds and write them below.

Today is my birthday. I hope to have a fun day. Five friends are coming to my party. We will play pin the tail on the donkey. We will also eat cake and ice cream. I am excited to open presents. I wish for a new hockey stick.

Short Vowel Words

wish	have	will
a	stick	pin
fun	presents	is

Write a sentence using 3 of the short vowel words from above.

16

Page 16

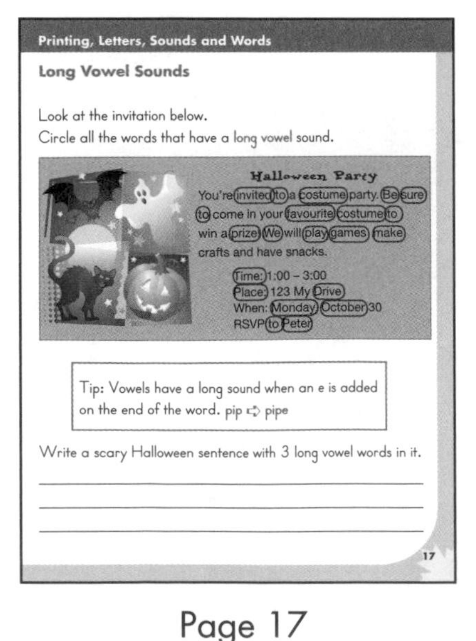
Printing, Letters, Sounds and Words

Long Vowel Sounds

Look at the invitation below.
Circle all the words that have a long vowel sound.

Halloween Party
You're invited to a costume party. Be sure to come in your favourite costume to win a prize. We will play games, make crafts and have snacks.
Time: 1:00 – 3:00
Place: 123 My Drive
When: Monday, October 30
RSVP to Peter

Tip: Vowels have a long sound when an e is added on the end of the word. pip ➪ pipe

Write a scary Halloween sentence with 3 long vowel words in it.

17

Page 17

Printing, Letters, Sounds and Words

Word Families

Word families are words that end in the same letters but begin with different letters. These are four different word families.

_at _ad _an _ay

Fill in the beginning letters to make words for each of the following word families. The first one is done for you.

at	ad	an	ay
c at	d ad	r an	h ay
b at	b ad	c an	d ay
s at	s ad	f an	l ay
h at	h ad	m an	m ay
f at	m ad	p an	p ay

Words in the same family rhyme.

18

Page 18

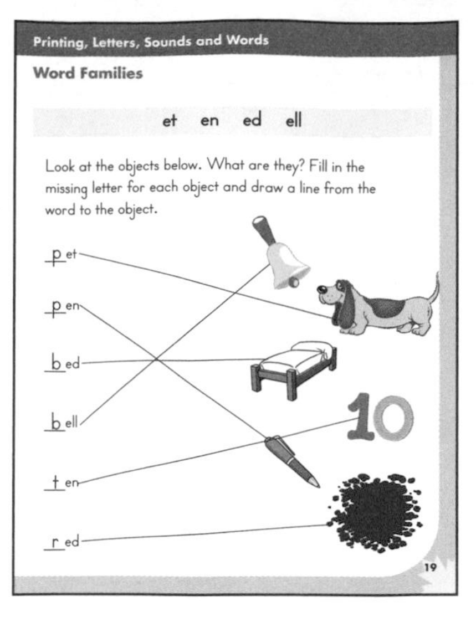

Printing, Letters, Sounds and Words

Word Families

et en ed ell

Look at the objects below. What are they? Fill in the missing letter for each object and draw a line from the word to the object.

p et
p en
b ed
b ell
t en
r ed

19

Page 19

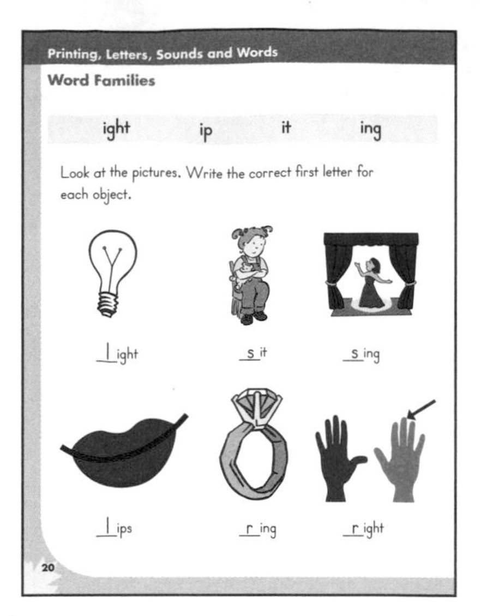

Printing, Letters, Sounds and Words

Word Families

ight ip it ing

Look at the pictures. Write the correct first letter for each object.

l ight
s it
s ing
l ips
r ing
r ight

20

Page 20

Printing, Letters, Sounds and Words

Word Families

old op ow oy

Look at the pictures. Write the correct first letter for each object.

p op
b oy
f old
c ow
t oys
h op

21

Page 21

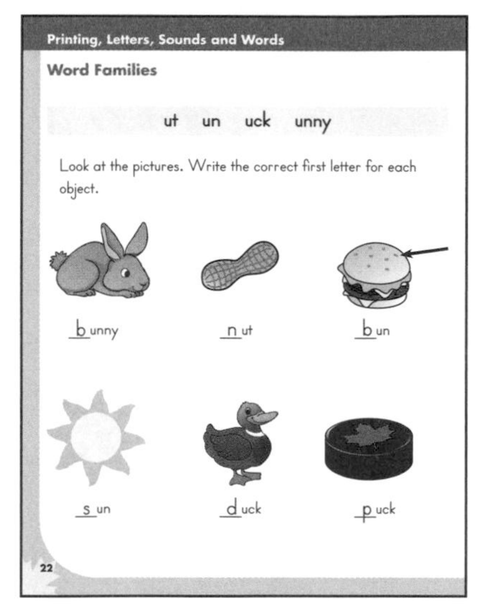

Printing, Letters, Sounds and Words

Word Families

ut un uck unny

Look at the pictures. Write the correct first letter for each object.

b unny
n ut
b un
s un
d uck
p uck

22

Page 22

Printing, Letters, Sounds and Words

Blends

th

When th are together, they make one sound as in **that** or **with**.

Complete the words by adding th .

1. t h is
2. t h e
3. t h ere
4. pa t h
5. ba t h

Some words have th in the middle.

tooth**brush** some**thing** mathematics

Can you think of a word with th in the middle?

birthday

23

Page 23

Printing, Letters, Sounds and Words

Blends

sh

When sh are seen together, they make one sound such as in shelf or wash.

Complete the words by adding sh.

1. s h ape
2. fi s h
3. s h ell
4. bru s h
5. s h eep

Can you think of some words that begin or end with sh?

24

Page 24

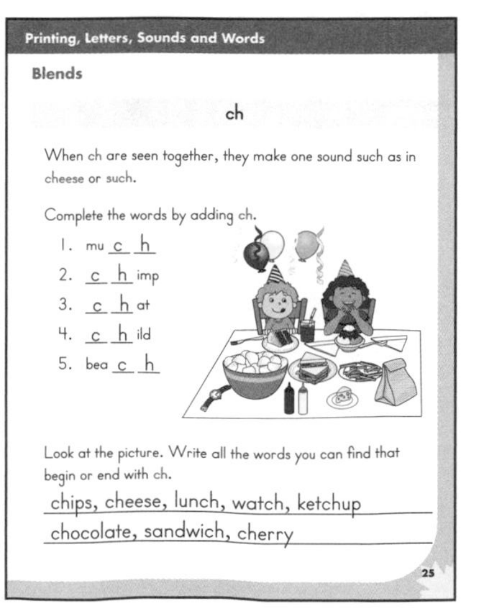

Printing, Letters, Sounds and Words

Blends

ch

When ch are seen together, they make one sound such as in cheese or such.

Complete the words by adding ch.

1. mu c h
2. c h imp
3. c h at
4. c h ild
5. bea c h

Look at the picture. Write all the words you can find that begin or end with ch.

chips, cheese, lunch, watch, ketchup
chocolate, sandwich, cherry

25

Page 25

Printing, Letters, Sounds and Words

Compound Words

Two words put together to make one word are compound words.
Some examples are: **sun**burn **out**side **bed**time

Look at the pictures below. Name each picture.
Put the words together to make compound words.

sailboat
beehive
broomstick
hairbrush

26

Page 26

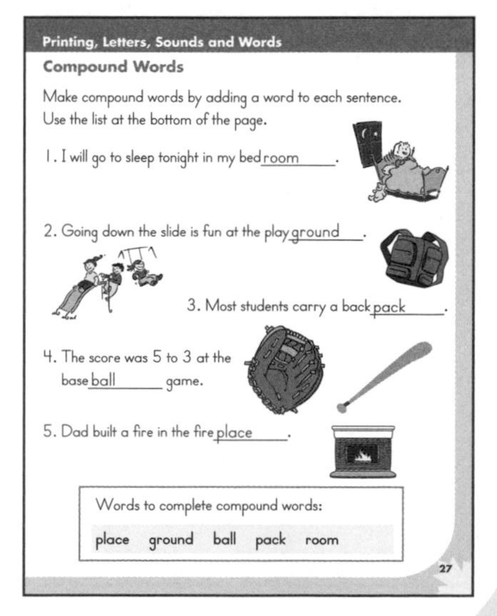

Printing, Letters, Sounds and Words

Compound Words

Make compound words by adding a word to each sentence.
Use the list at the bottom of the page.

1. I will go to sleep tonight in my bed room .
2. Going down the slide is fun at the play ground .
3. Most students carry a back pack .
4. The score was 5 to 3 at the base ball game.
5. Dad built a fire in the fire place .

Words to complete compound words:
place ground ball pack room

27

Page 27

Solutions

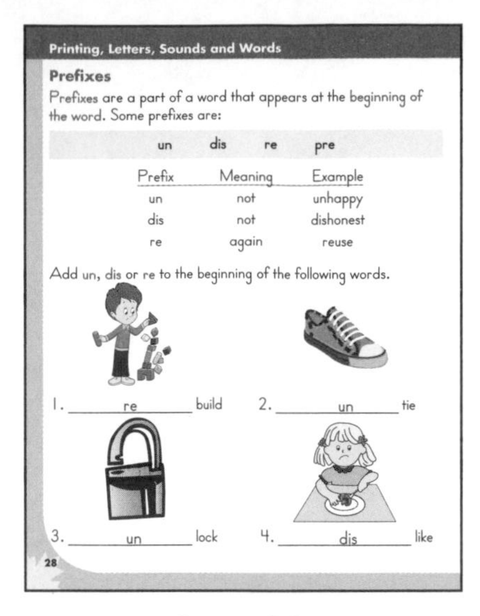
Printing, Letters, Sounds and Words

Prefixes

Prefixes are a part of a word that appears at the beginning of the word. Some prefixes are:

un dis re pre

Prefix	Meaning	Example
un	not	unhappy
dis	not	dishonest
re	again	reuse

Add un, dis or re to the beginning of the following words.

1. re build
2. un tie
3. un lock
4. dis like

28

Page 28

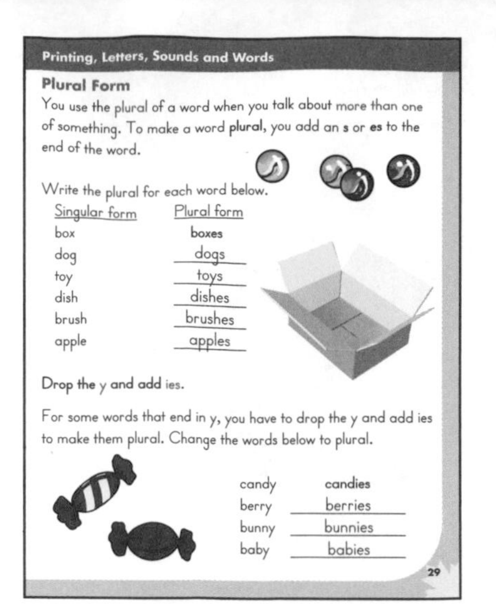
Printing, Letters, Sounds and Words

Plural Form

You use the plural of a word when you talk about more than one of something. To make a word **plural**, you add an **s** or **es** to the end of the word.

Write the plural for each word below.

Singular form	Plural form
box	boxes
dog	dogs
toy	toys
dish	dishes
brush	brushes
apple	apples

Drop the y **and add** ies.

For some words that end in y, you have to drop the y and add ies to make them plural. Change the words below to plural.

candy	candies
berry	berries
bunny	bunnies
baby	babies

29

Page 29

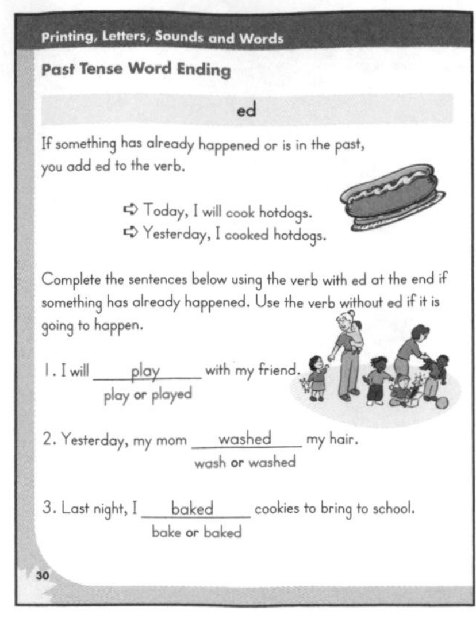
Printing, Letters, Sounds and Words

Past Tense Word Ending

ed

If something has already happened or is in the past, you add ed to the verb.

➪ Today, I will cook hotdogs.
➪ Yesterday, I cooked hotdogs.

Complete the sentences below using the verb with ed at the end if something has already happened. Use the verb without ed if it is going to happen.

1. I will play with my friend. (play or played)
2. Yesterday, my mom washed my hair. (wash or washed)
3. Last night, I baked cookies to bring to school. (bake or baked)

30

Page 30

Grammar

Parts of Speech – Common Nouns

A common noun is a person, place or thing.
The words dog, pot and lake are all common nouns.

Circle the common nouns.

(hill) (ball) (fish) and (car) fast sad (house) slow (backyard)

Noun Search

Circle the nouns in each sentence.
The first one is done.

1. The (car) drove very fast.
2. Most (frogs) are green.
3. The (kids) ran up the (hill).
4. (Dogs) like to walk in the (park).
5. (Clowns) can do magic (tricks).

31

Page 31

Grammar

Parts of Speech – Common Nouns

Search for the common nouns.

Look at the picture above. Write all the common nouns you see.

bus	stores
police car	restaurant
fire hydrant	street
stop sign	sidewalk
and more	

32

Page 32

Grammar

Parts of Speech – Pronouns

A pronoun is another word for a person, place or thing.
Pronouns are used instead of naming a person, place or thing.
Some pronouns are: she, he, it, they, I, us, me.

Using the following pronouns, complete the sentences.

we us me I he she it they

1. She had fun at the party.
2. Sammy played with me yesterday.
3. I got an A on my math test.
4. They took their hockey sticks to the park.

Write your own sentence using a pronoun.

33

Page 33

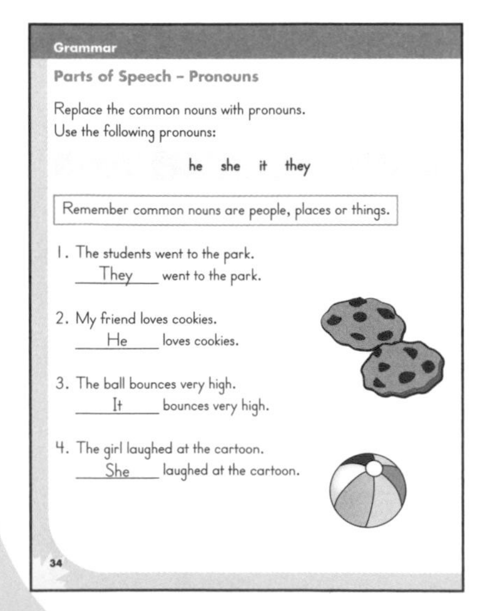
Grammar

Parts of Speech – Pronouns

Replace the common nouns with pronouns.
Use the following pronouns:

he she it they

Remember common nouns are people, places or things.

1. The students went to the park.
   They went to the park.
2. My friend loves cookies.
   He loves cookies.
3. The ball bounces very high.
   It bounces very high.
4. The girl laughed at the cartoon.
   She laughed at the cartoon.

34

Page 34

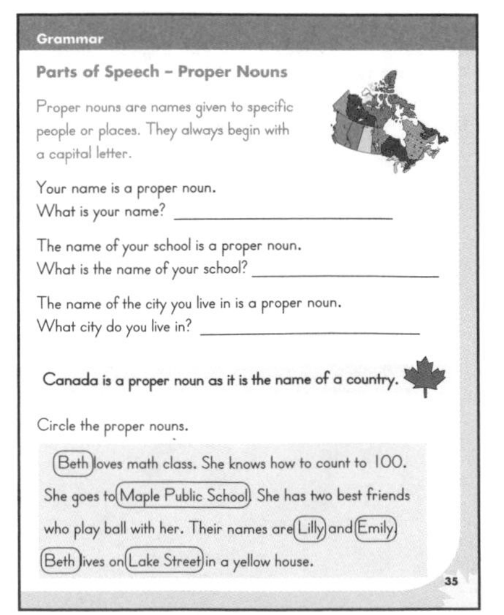
Grammar

Parts of Speech – Proper Nouns

Proper nouns are names given to specific people or places. They always begin with a capital letter.

Your name is a proper noun.
What is your name? ____________

The name of your school is a proper noun.
What is the name of your school? ____________

The name of the city you live in is a proper noun.
What city do you live in? ____________

Canada is a proper noun as it is the name of a country.

Circle the proper nouns.

(Beth) loves math class. She knows how to count to 100. She goes to (Maple Public School). She has two best friends who play ball with her. Their names are (Lilly) and (Emily). (Beth) lives on (Lake Street) in a yellow house.

35

Page 35

Grammar

Parts of Speech – Adjectives

Adjectives describe people, places or things.

happy boy, big hat, red mittens, one crayon, small dog

Silly Sentences

Choose adjectives from below or choose your own to make silly sentences.

1. The clown has big feet and a red nose.
2. At the party, we ate delicious cake and played fun games.
3. My mommy read me a good book with colourful pictures.

Adjectives

delicious	fun	amazing	huge
yucky	silly	colourful	noisy
red	crazy	sad	funny
big	good	scary	happy

36

Page 36

Solutions

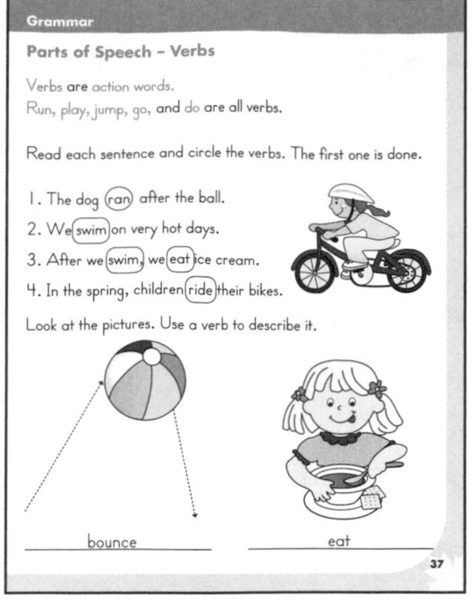
Grammar

Parts of Speech – Verbs

Verbs are action words.
Run, play, jump, go, and do are all verbs.

Read each sentence and circle the verbs. The first one is done.

1. The dog (ran) after the ball.
2. We (swim) on very hot days.
3. After we (swim), we (eat) ice cream.
4. In the spring, children (ride) their bikes.

Look at the pictures. Use a verb to describe it.

bounce   eat

37

Page 37

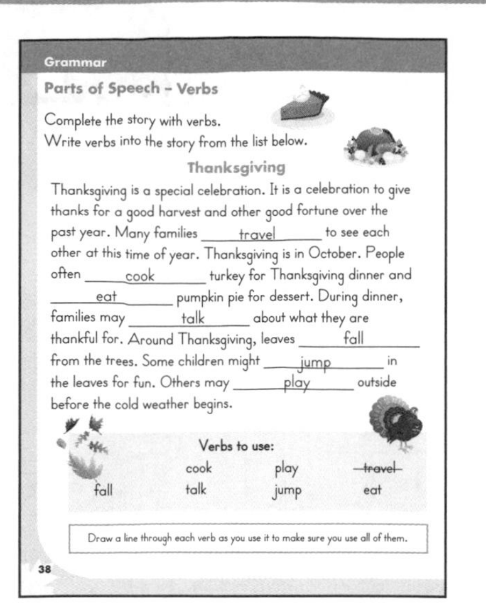
Grammar

Parts of Speech – Verbs

Complete the story with verbs.
Write verbs into the story from the list below.

Thanksgiving

Thanksgiving is a special celebration. It is a celebration to give thanks for a good harvest and other good fortune over the past year. Many families __travel__ to see each other at this time of year. Thanksgiving is in October. People often __cook__ turkey for Thanksgiving dinner and __eat__ pumpkin pie for dessert. During dinner, families may __talk__ about what they are thankful for. Around Thanksgiving, leaves __fall__ from the trees. Some children might __jump__ in the leaves for fun. Others may __play__ outside before the cold weather begins.

Verbs to use:
cook play ~~travel~~
fall talk jump eat

Draw a line through each verb as you use it to make sure you use all of them.

38

Page 38

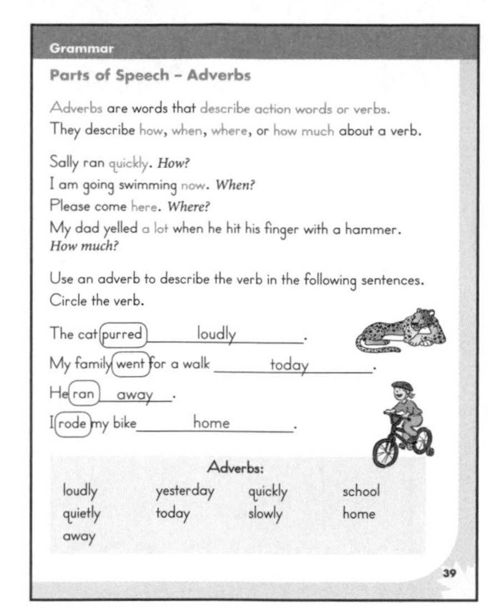
Grammar

Parts of Speech – Adverbs

Adverbs are words that describe action words or verbs.
They describe how, when, where, or how much about a verb.

Sally ran quickly. *How?*
I am going swimming now. *When?*
Please come here. *Where?*
My dad yelled a lot when he hit his finger with a hammer. *How much?*

Use an adverb to describe the verb in the following sentences. Circle the verb.

The cat (purred) __loudly__.
My family (went) for a walk __today__.
He (ran) __away__.
I (rode) my bike __home__.

Adverbs:
loudly yesterday quickly school
quietly today slowly home
away

39

Page 39

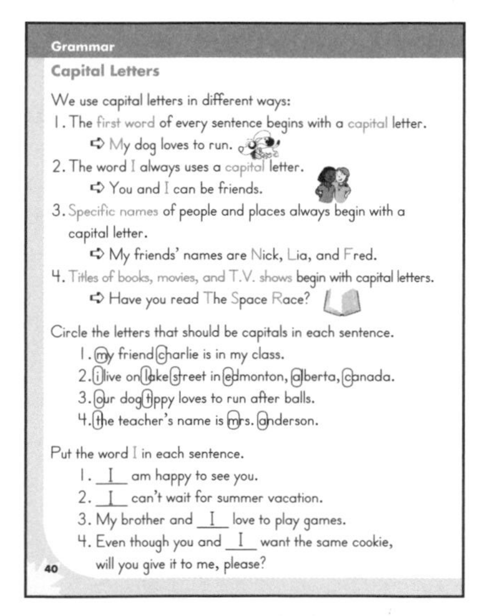
Grammar

Capital Letters

We use capital letters in different ways:
1. The first word of every sentence begins with a capital letter.
➪ My dog loves to run.
2. The word I always uses a capital letter.
➪ You and I can be friends.
3. Specific names of people and places always begin with a capital letter.
➪ My friends' names are Nick, Lia, and Fred.
4. Titles of books, movies, and T.V. shows begin with capital letters.
➪ Have you read The Space Race?

Circle the letters that should be capitals in each sentence.
1. (m)y friend (c)harlie is in my class.
2. (i) live on (l)ake (s)treet in (e)dmonton, (a)lberta, (c)anada.
3. (o)ur dog (f)lppy loves to run after balls.
4. (t)he teacher's name is (m)rs. (a)nderson.

Put the word I in each sentence.
1. __I__ am happy to see you.
2. __I__ can't wait for summer vacation.
3. My brother and __I__ love to play games.
4. Even though you and __I__ want the same cookie, will you give it to me, please?

40

Page 40

Grammar

Sentence Punctuation

. ? !

All sentences start with a capital letter. A telling sentence ends with a period. ➪ You are my friend.

An exciting telling sentence ends with an exclamation mark!
➪ I won a prize!

A question ends with a question mark?
➪ Are you going to the park?

Put a ., ?, or a ! at the end of each sentence.
1. Our country is called Canada __.__
2. What is the name of your city __?__
3. My sister's name is Michelle __.__
4. My birthday is today __!__
5. When are you coming to my house __?__
6. The score was close but our soccer team won the game __!__

41

Page 41

Grammar

Synonyms

Synonyms are words that mean the same thing.
Big and large are synonyms.

Choose the Synonym

Read the first word. Circle another word that is a synonym.
The first one is done.

fast	slow	run	(quick)
happy	shy	(glad)	sad
laugh	funny	cry	(chuckle)
skinny	(thin)	fat	small
tiny	large	big	(small)
shy	courage	happy	(bashful)
scared	silly	(afraid)	Halloween

42

Page 42

Grammar

Synonym Word Search

B I G L N A D A
T S A F L K N N
Q P T L I D E G
Y U A E A A I R
G M I T P M R Y
S U I C F R F T
F N R I K C A E
Y G L A R G E C

ANGRY FAST MAD RUG
BIG FRIEND PAL SMALL
CARPET LARGE QUICK TINY

43

Page 43

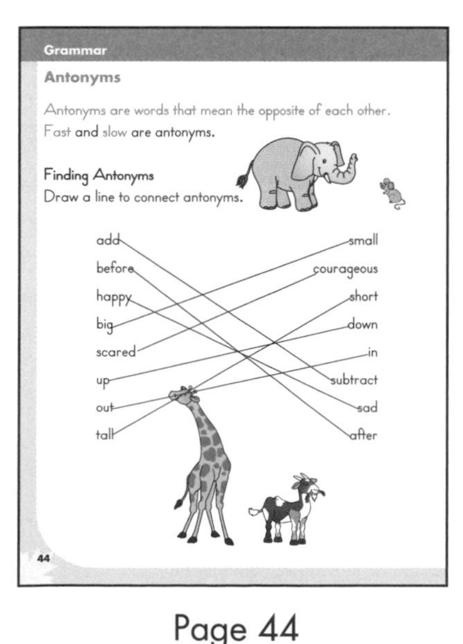
Grammar

Antonyms

Antonyms are words that mean the opposite of each other.
Fast and slow are antonyms.

Finding Antonyms
Draw a line to connect antonyms.

add small
before courageous
happy short
big down
scared in
up subtract
out sad
tall after

44

Page 44

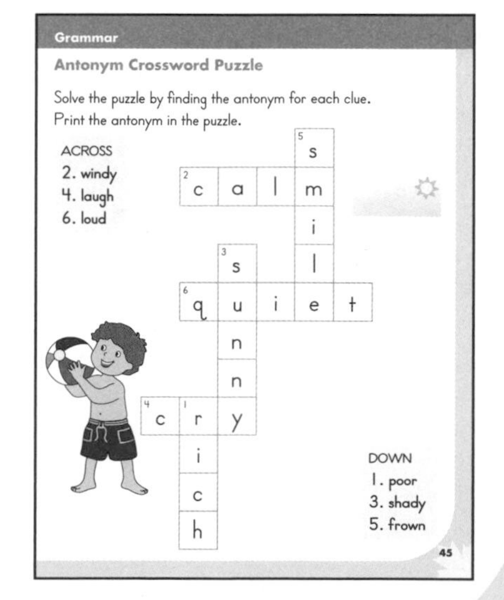
Grammar

Antonym Crossword Puzzle

Solve the puzzle by finding the antonym for each clue.
Print the antonym in the puzzle.

ACROSS
2. windy — calm
4. laugh — cry
6. loud — quiet

DOWN
1. poor — rich
3. shady — sunny
5. frown — smile

45

Page 45

BOOKAROO
BAKERY
BARBER
GROCERY